'That was quite an entrance.'

Axel looked up. 'Now I would be grateful if you would make an equally stunning exit.'

In response Katrina took a further couple of steps into the room and glared at the dark-suited figure.

'Your secretary said you were in a meeting. I can't see any meeting. There's nobody here but you.'

'And you, it would appear. One too many.'

Dear Reader

Well, summer is almost upon us. Time to think about holidays, perhaps? Where to go? What to do? And how to get everything you own into one suitcase! Wherever you decide to go, don't forget to pack plenty of Mills & Boon novels. This month's selection includes such exotic locations as Andalucía, Brazil and the Aegean Islands, so you can enjoy lots of holiday romance even if you stay at home!

The Editor

Stephanie Howard was born and brought up in Dundee in Scotland, and educated at the London School of Economics. For ten years she worked as a journalist in London on a variety of women's magazines, among them *Woman's Own*, and was latterly editor of the now-defunct *Honey*. She has spent many years living and working abroad—in Italy, Malaysia, the Philippines and in the Middle East.

Recent titles by the same author:

COUNTERFEIT LOVE
CONSPIRACY OF LOVE
A SCANDALOUS AFFAIR

BEWARE A LOVER'S LIE

BY
STEPHANIE HOWARD

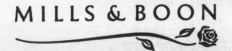

MILLS & BOON LIMITED
ETON HOUSE, 18-24 PARADISE ROAD
RICHMOND, SURREY TW9 1SR

First published in Great Britain 1994
by Mills & Boon Limited

© Stephanie Howard 1994

Australian copyright 1994
Philippine copyright 1994
This edition 1994

ISBN 0 263 78511 4

Set in Times Roman 11 on 12 pt.
01-9406-48777 C

Made and printed in Great Britain

CHAPTER ONE

'KINDLY wait here, *señorita*. Señor Jerez will be with you shortly.'

'Thank you.'

Katrina smiled and nodded politely as the woman disappeared back inside the splendid villa. Then she stepped to the edge of the wide stone-flagged terrace that overlooked the breathtaking blue of the sea. She leaned against the railings and drank in the morning air, feeling the warmth of the sun caress her lightly freckled face and the breeze gently ruffle her long red hair.

So, this was the island of Tenerife. More like paradise, she was thinking!

Then she smiled to herself as the irony struck her. Here, in the midst of paradise, she had an appointment with the devil!

At that very moment there was a movement behind her. She turned curiously. Surely it couldn't be Axel Jerez already? She'd been certain he'd make a point of keeping her waiting.

But the man she was looking at was indeed Axel Jerez. Though this was their first meeting Katrina knew that instinctively. As she looked into his face, a jolt went through her.

And then he spoke. 'I'm Axel Jerez. This is most unexpected . . . but welcome to my home.'

He was stepping towards her, one hand extended, a light, ambiguous smile on his lips. And as she met his dark gaze, Katrina found herself immobilised by the fierce, overwhelming power of the man.

He was even taller than she had expected, more athletically built, with wide muscular shoulders and a deep strong chest. Even beneath the light shirt and trousers he was wearing, she could tell he possessed an impressive physique.

But it was not the power of his physique that had glued Katrina to the spot, but the incredible power that radiated from his face. Every line of his arrogant, dark-tanned features proclaimed the character of their owner—harsh and passionate and full of secrets.

His hair was as black as midnight, but his eyes were even blacker—twin pools of endless midnight darkness that sent a shiver of uneasiness rushing through her. Those eyes were filled with an aura of lurking menace.

Irene was right, Katrina automatically found herself thinking. For she could see for herself now why her sister had dubbed Axel *el diablo*—the devil!

Out loud, she said, 'I'm pleased to meet you. I'm Katrina MacGregor, Irene's sister.' Overcoming her momentary paralysis, she held out her hand to him.

The clasp of his hand was cool and firm and fleeting, yet that brief physical contact was like a shock to Katrina's system. Her fingers were on fire as she snatched them away.

Again, that ambiguous smile touched the wide passionate lips. 'Shall we sit?' Axel indicated with a wave of his hand a group of cane armchairs arranged round a low cane table. 'I think it would be more comfortable than standing.' Then he added, leading her towards them, taking her agreement for granted, 'I've asked my housekeeper to bring us something to drink.'

Katrina followed, watching him through narrowed green eyes. He possessed the easy, unselfconscious assurance of a man who knew he was totally in control. In control of his life and of his surroundings—and of every single being who had the misfortune to stray into them.

Well, he may just be in for a surprise, she told herself. For there's no way in the world he's going to control me!

Axel waited politely until she had seated herself, then unhurriedly he lowered himself into one of the chairs opposite her.

'So, what brings you to Tenerife?' he enquired, leaning back and watching her through those eyes as black as whirlpools. 'Are you here, like so many of your compatriots, on holiday?'

Katrina found herself licking her lips before answering. The question had been asked in a tone that was carefully casual, yet he'd been unable to disguise the hostility in his eyes. As polite as he was being, he was not pleased to see her.

'No, I'm not here on holiday.' Katrina crossed her long legs, smoothing her calf-length skirt over her knees. 'The main reason I'm here is because of work. I have a job to do on the island. But while I'm here...' She paused for a moment, feeling a sense of sadness as she thought of her second, more personal task. 'But while I'm here,' she resumed, 'there's something I have to do for Irene.'

'Irene.'

He pronounced the name as though it were something offensive. Not surprising, Katrina thought, in view of what Irene had told her. She felt thankful that the coincidence of her business trip to the island had spared her poor sister the agony of coming back herself. For it appeared Irene hadn't been exaggerating. Axel really did dislike her.

Axel was watching Katrina, his fingers laced across his chest, his hands very dark against the light blue of his shirt. 'Somehow I suspected,' he observed now, crushingly, 'that your sudden appearance might have something to do with Irene.'

'Irene and Jaime.' Katrina kept her gaze steady and ignored the harsh bite in his voice. 'Jaime, your brother,' she added for the sake of clarity.

'Yes, I had guessed it was that Jaime.' He smiled an amused smile, full of quick, unexpected charm. Then, as suddenly as it had appeared, the smile had vanished and he was narrowing his eyes at her again. 'Though, for all I know, your sister may have been acquainted with many Jaimes.'

There was a slur in that remark. Katrina felt herself bridle. 'No,' she shot back, straightening in her seat. 'My sister was acquainted with only one Jaime.'

For a moment they faced one another across the cane table, eyes locked in mutual disapproval and antipathy. And suddenly Katrina was doubly determined to keep the promise she had made her sister—to right the wrong that Jaime had done her—even if it meant fighting Axel every inch of the way. Which, it was growing clearer every minute, was precisely what it would mean!

But, just at that moment, the housekeeper reappeared.

'Our drinks,' Axel pronounced, his eyes still fixed on Katrina, as the handsome middle-aged woman who had greeted Katrina on her arrival now proceeded to lay out glasses and a jug of fruit juice on the glass-topped cane table that stood between them.

'I hope you like pomegranate juice?' he added. 'If not, Pilar can always get you something else.'

The offer was delivered with another flash of charm, so powerful and unexpected that Katrina smiled back at him. 'I've never had it before, but I'm sure I'll like it,' she assured him. 'I'm very fond of pomegranates.'

'In that case, there's no problem.' Axel nodded to the housekeeper, who proceeded to pour two glasses of the pale pink liquid. 'Besides, Pilar's pomegranate juice is the best you'll ever taste.'

As the woman smiled, he turned to her. 'That's all for now, *gracias*.' Then, still in that warm tone, he added something in Spanish.

Katrina watched him beneath her lashes, feeling a twinge of confusion and a sense that she had slightly misjudged her adversary. Irene had told her he was a monster. *El diablo*. The devil. And, without too much difficulty, Katrina could see what she meant. But she had not been prepared for the subtle charm of the man that he could switch on and off with the suddenness of a light.

Though I ought to have known he'd have charm, she told herself. The devil's charm is part of what makes him so dangerous!

'You're not at all like your sister, you know.'

As he spoke, he had turned to look at her, and the sudden impact of those dark eyes had caused Katrina's heart to jump. She reached for her fruit juice, dropping her gaze away. 'I know,' she told him, as she took a quick gulp.

'You're rather more as I would imagine a typical Scot—that blazing red hair, those freckles, the green eyes. You look as though you've just stepped out of some heathery Scottish glen.'

'Well, I haven't. As a matter of fact, I live in the centre of Edinburgh.'

Again that flash of a quick smile touched his eyes. The wide, sensuous lips curled at the corners. 'It was meant as a compliment,' he told her. 'I'm rather partial to heathery Scottish glens. And to redheads.'

'How interesting.' Katrina took another nervous gulp of her pomegranate juice, knowing she'd flushed crimson and hating herself for being so stupid. Then she added, steering the conversation away from his personal preferences, 'I get the red hair from my father. Irene's darker colouring is more like our mother.'

Axel continued to watch her, the smile flickering round his lips. 'If you take after your father, he must be a very handsome man.'

'I suppose he is.' Again she felt a flush rise and quickly took another mouthful of her drink.

'I see you like the pomegranate juice, after all.' Axel's eyes slid to the glass she held so tightly in her hand. 'You've drunk almost all of it already.'

Out of sheer foolish nervousness, Katrina chastised herself silently, wondering why on earth she should be nervous in the first place.

I'm not nervous, just a little uneasy, that's all, she excused herself. I feel thrown. He's not what I was expecting.

Very deliberately, she laid her glass down on the table. 'Yes, I do like it,' she told him. 'It's quite delicious.' The flush had gone from her cheeks. Her gaze was steady. She sat back in her seat, in control of herself again. 'It's just what you need on a hot day like this.'

'Yes, it is quite hot. A little hotter, I expect, than Edinburgh?'

'A great deal hotter than Edinburgh.' Katrina smiled wryly. It had felt wonderful yesterday evening to step off the plane into a deliciously balmy seventy-five degrees—about ten degrees hotter than midday Edinburgh! 'Even in mid-July, I'm afraid, Scotland isn't exactly famous for its tropical weather.'

'Indeed it isn't.' The dark eyes were watching her, seeming to caress the halo of bright red hair that fell to almost halfway down her back, then pausing to examine her fine-boned face with its straight, shapely nose and soft-lipped mouth. And again Katrina felt a flush rise to her throat, but this time, determinedly, she conquered it.

He's a ladies' man, she thought. A regular Don Juan. Well practised in the art of bringing a blush to women's cheeks.

She felt better for the disapproval that accompanied that thought and instantly a great deal safer. She was not the type of young woman who responded to such men.

'So, what do you do in non-tropical Edinburgh?' Axel steepled his fingers, resting his chin on their tips. 'Do you, unlike your sister, pursue some kind of career?'

That was another subtle slur against Irene, Katrina sensed. Again she felt herself bridle in defence as she shot at him, 'Had it not been for your brother, my sister might have a career! And that, as a matter of fact, is what I've come here to talk about!'

'All in good time.' He had held up his hand. 'First, I want to know something about who I'm dealing with.' His tone was soft enough, but his eyes were tempered steel. 'We can get down to other matters in a moment.'

Katrina could have insisted that they get down to other matters now, but to take that line would be a total waste of time. The charm had gone, melted like snow. In its place stood a wall, and a will, of iron. He would not budge an inch until he was ready.

She sat back in her seat, holding her gaze steady. Why should she fight him? She was in no hurry. And there'd be plenty of time for fighting later.

'I'm in television,' she told him. 'I'm a researcher.'

'National TV?'

'No, a local station. I've been with them now for a couple of years.'

'Interesting work, I imagine?'

'Extremely interesting.' Katrina nodded and smiled. She loved her job.

'So, what have you come to Tenerife to research?' The long tanned fingers dropped from his chin to the chair arms. 'You said you were here partly because of work.'

'Yes, I did.' She hesitated before continuing, wondering at the wisdom of revealing too much. But then, dismissing caution—what harm could it do?—she went on to tell him, 'We're doing a series of programmes on Scots living abroad. I've come to meet one who lives here on Tenerife.'

'I see.' He did not appear overly interested. Instead he said, 'What drew you into research work? I would have thought you would have done rather well on the other side of the cameras.'

It was another of those compliments that she had already guessed were his speciality. The kind that were designed to flatter her and make her blush.

But she neither blushed nor felt flattered. 'Research is what interests me,' she told him. 'I'm not tempted by the false glamour of having my face on the screen.'

'What a pity. Your false modesty is undoubtedly the viewers' loss. If I were your boss, I'd insist you take a screen test.'

'Mine did and I refused.'

'Ah, but I would not take no for an answer.'

'I'm afraid you would have to, just as he did.'

But as she said it Katrina felt the skin at the back of her neck tingle. He was looking at her so directly that it was as though he had touched her. And the look in his eyes was half challenge, half warning. My will, he was telling her, is not so easy to resist. Don't fool yourself. You would do as I wished.

She felt the need to repeat, as something flared inside her, 'I'm afraid you would have no more success than he did.'

Axel smiled a cool smile. 'I think,' he told her softly, 'you would find, if you put it to the test, that you're wrong about that.'

In that moment, as she looked back at him and felt the ruthless power in him, a sudden anxious chill spread through Katrina's heart. She had known he would not be an easy man to deal with. Irene had already warned her of that. But now she was wondering if she had any chance at all of keeping the promise she'd made her sister, and herself. One thing was for sure. She had a battle on her hands.

But that battle was yet to come. She shook the feeling from her and returned to the verbal skirmish of the present.

'I'm afraid I'm just not interested in doing screen tests. Not everyone is out for fame and glory, you know.'

'Like me, you mean?'

That was precisely what she had meant, though she would never have dreamt of being so impolite as to say it. And she felt slightly thrown at the way he had picked up her innuendo and tossed it back at her with a smile of amusement.

She said hurriedly, though it was probably the wrong thing to say, 'Irene's told me about all the media attention you get, and about how you——'

'Lap it up,' he finished for her. 'I imagine that's the description your sister would use?'

Katrina could not fault his imagination. She'd been about to say 'enjoy it'—but 'lap it up' was word for word the description Irene had used!

Axel laughed, a brief, dismissive bark of laughter. 'You call agreeing to the occasional interview on Spanish TV lapping up fame and glory?' he asked her. 'If my ego was so hungry for reassurance that it had to rely on scraps like that, I think you could say I'd be in a pretty sorry state.'

Katrina grimaced, somehow sensing that what he said was true. The monumental ego of Axel Jerez would need no such scrawny offerings to make it flourish. It was so huge and powerful that it probably fed itself.

She said defensively, 'But you do like appearing on TV?'

'Whether I like it or not, I do appear occasionally. The media occasionally demands my comments about this or that.'

'This or that, I presume, being your various business concerns? Your hotel chain... Your new airline...'

'Well, I certainly don't encourage queries about my private life...' He paused and smiled a grim, humourless smile. 'The only questions I ever answer are those of a business nature.'

Then his expression softened. 'About which you appear to know a fair bit.' He smiled his congratulations. 'I see you've done your research.'

'It's second nature.' Katrina smiled back at him. 'Or perhaps, more accurately, it's my professional training. Like you, I like to know all I can about who I'm dealing with.'

But, as she said it, inside Katrina was frowning. His remark about not encouraging personal questions had instantly struck a chord within her. For though Irene had been able to supply in some detail information about his high-flying business career, not to mention plenty of damning comments on his character, she'd had little or nothing to reveal about his personal life.

'Oh, that's a closed book,' she'd said when Katrina had pressed her. 'He never discusses it and neither does Jaime. I've heard stories that he has half a dozen wives tucked away and other stories that say he has no fixed woman in his life.' She'd wrinkled her nose. 'My guess is it's the latter. After all, no woman would have him!'

That last bit was plainly nonsense. Katrina could see for herself now that Axel Jerez was powerfully attractive. He wasn't *her* type, of course. She found his arrogance unbearable. But if he was free, there would surely be no shortage of women—women with rather less discriminating standards!—who were more than likely falling over themselves to have him!

And though suddenly she was curious—was he married or was he single?—she knew far better than to broach the subject. He hadn't been joking about not encouraging personal questions. And he'd meant not from anyone, not only the media.

He was leaning forward in his chair, reaching for his glass. Watching her over the top of it, he raised it to his lips. 'So, now,' he said, 'that we each know who we're dealing with, perhaps you'd like to go ahead and tell me what you're here for? Quite clearly you haven't just dropped by to pass on your sister's good wishes?'

'No, I'm afraid I haven't.'

'That would somewhat have surprised me.' He laid down his glass, but continued to lean forward, smiling slightly, dark eyes fixed on Katrina's, making her suddenly illogically glad that the solid-

looking cane table stood between them. There was
something oddly threatening about that look in his
eyes.

'But I confess,' he continued, 'I'm somewhat
surprised anyway. I hadn't expected ever to hear of
your sister again. I had thought she was an episode
thankfully consigned to the past.'

'An episode? Is that how you think of my sister?'
Katrina felt deeply offended on Irene's behalf and
made no bones about allowing her offence to show.
'But I suppose that's precisely the callous sort of
attitude I should have expected from Jaime's older
brother.'

'I would say it is, too, yet you sound disapproving.' Axel continued to lean towards her as he
spoke, one curved dark eyebrow lifting inquisi-
torially. 'What attitude would you suggest I adopt
instead?'

'Perhaps a more compassionate one would be
more fitting. I suppose you know that your brother
has broken my sister's heart?'

Axel let out another sharp bark of laughter. 'No,'
he smiled, 'I'm afraid I didn't. But now that I do,
I shall certainly try to be more compassionate.'

Katrina looked back at him, tight-lipped, faintly
shocked by his reaction. 'Somehow, I doubt you're
capable of that,' she said.

He made no effort to deny it. On the contrary,
he confirmed it. He folded his arms across his chest.
'You're right. In your sister's regard, I am quite
incapable.'

'Why? Do you think she deserved your brother's
infidelity? Do you think she deserved to be dropped
for someone else?'

A flicker crossed Axel's eyes, a flicker of something dark and dangerous. And Katrina could feel the sudden tension in him springing from every line of his body. Quite involuntarily, she felt herself shrinking away from him, pressing herself back against the cushions.

Then he took a deep breath and spoke. 'Your sister knew what she was getting into. My brother never made her any promises. She had her eyes wide open. She knew the score.'

'And what is that supposed to mean? Irene knew no such thing. She had no idea your brother was a philanderer and a liar.'

Again there was a flash of that dark look in his eyes, then his mouth twisted angrily as he told her, 'She knew their little affair was just a passing fancy. They both agreed on that. It was never meant to be serious. Both of them knew it was nothing more than a brief fling.'

'Says who?' Katrina was indignant. Her green eyes flashed at him. 'If you'd seen the state my sister was in when she returned to Scotland, virtually on the edge of a nervous breakdown, you wouldn't be coming out with that sort of nonsense!'

'A nervous breakdown? Don't give me that rubbish. Either your sister's having you on or else you're joking.' The black eyes looked back at her, as cold as a reptile's. 'It was clear from the beginning the affair was never meant to last. They both went into it just to have a bit of fun.'

'Is that what you believe? Is that what your brother told you?' Angrily, Katrina frowned and shook her head at him. 'If it is, it's your brother who's having *you* on. My sister wasn't just looking for a bit of fun. I hardly think she'd have stayed on here for nearly a year in order to be with him if that was all she was after. She happens to be in love with your brother!'

'Next you'll be telling me she was expecting marriage!' Axel laughed dismissively as though nothing could be more outrageous. Then he paused and fixed Katrina with a hard, dissecting look. 'I met your sister on several occasions. I could see what type of girl she was.'

'And what type of girl was that?' Katrina was seething. She glared at him, daring him to insult Irene further.

He proceeded to do so without batting one long black eyelash.

'The type of girl, as I told you, who's simply looking for a good time. All she was interested in was dragging Jaime off to the disco or to some fancy restaurant or to the latest nightspot. As far as I could see, she didn't have a serious bone in her body. She wasn't even capable of holding down a proper job.'

'I've never heard such malicious nonsense!' But suddenly Katrina understood. 'You're glad your brother dumped her and went off with someone else. You never liked her. Irene told me. Right from the start, you kept trying to break them up.'

'No, I never liked her and I did try to break them up and I'm heartily glad it's finally over.' Axel paused to pierce her with a malicious black look. 'So, don't expect me to weep any tears over her supposedly broken heart.'

'No, I won't. As I said, I suspect you're incapable of compassion.' Through her anger, Katrina

forced herself to breathe deeply and slowly. 'But I
won't allow you to speak so insultingly about my
sister. She may be a bit wild at times, but she's not
what you're saying.'

'You mean she's not a tramp?'

It was like a slap in the face. Katrina looked back
at him in silence for a moment, quite winded.

'Well, you're entitled to your opinion, of course.
But *my* opinion is that she is.' Axel looked her
straight in the eyes as he said it. 'In my opinion
that's *precisely* what she is.'

'You have no right to say that.' Katrina was dry-
mouthed with anger. 'Your brother's the one who's
lacking in morals. *He*'s the one you ought to be
bad-mouthing.'

'You think so, do you?' Again that look touched
his eyes and again she could feel in him that flicker
of black tension. It was clear he deeply resented her
criticisms of his brother. And perhaps the reason
for that was the obvious one—that he was as bad
as Jaime, that they were two of a kind.

That's it, she thought. That's how they both treat
women—as temporary, disposable providers of
pleasure. And no doubt that was the reason why
Axel was so secretive about his private life. Because
he was a feckless, immoral gigolo, like his brother.

She straightened in her seat and eyed him with
disapproval. 'Now that I know what kind of family
your brother comes from, I would say my sister
had a lucky escape.'

'Then you have no cause for complaint and I
needn't detain you further.' He smiled in the face
of her subtle insult and, gripping the chair arms,

made as though to stand up. 'Now you can get on with interviewing your Scottish émigré.'

'Oh, but that's not why I came to see you... to complain about your brother's infidelity. That's between him and Irene. That's got nothing to do with me.'

'That's what I would have thought.' Axel paused and eyed her. 'So what was the reason you came to see me?'

'I came about the money. The money your brother took. It was money I lent my sister—and I mean to get it back.'

'Money? What money?' He looked genuinely baffled. For a moment his grip on the chair arms slackened. 'This is the first I've heard about any money.'

'It may well be.' Katrina somehow sensed it was. 'But, nevertheless, your brother's taken it. I lent it to Irene so they could start up a business together, but the business never happened, as you're obviously aware, and now your brother's disappeared with my sister's money.'

Axel was frowning across at her. 'What are you talking about, a business? My brother works for me and I'm absolutely sure he never contemplated going into business with your sister. He may sometimes lack judgement, but he's not a total idiot.'

'No, I suppose you probably think he's pretty clever, not only dumping Irene, but also tricking her out of her money!'

There was a silence as she glared into his dark, frowning face and he watched her in turn through narrowed jet-black eyes. Then, as he sat back in his seat, for the first time since she'd met him

Katrina felt the faintest flicker of hope that, after all, it might not come to a fight.

Unless he was an astonishingly good actor, it seemed pretty obvious that he'd known nothing whatsoever about the stolen money. Perhaps, once the revelation had had a moment to sink in, he'd be as outraged as she was and offer to help her get it back.

He said in a low voice. 'You'd better explain what you're talking about. For a start, what sort of sum of money are we talking about?'

'We're talking about the sum of six thousand pounds. I lent it to Irene a couple of months ago, before Jaime was distracted by this other girl he went off with. Irene told me she gave the money to Jaime. He was supposed to be looking after it while they looked for suitable premises for their business.'

'What premises? What business?' Axel's tone was sharp as he interrupted her. 'Kindly explain what the devil you're talking about!'

'They were looking for a small shop. Somewhere pretty modest. They were going to sell tourist stuff. Souvenirs, that sort of thing.'

'Not a very wise business move. There are too many already.'

'Well, that's not what Irene thought and that's not what she told me. She seemed pretty certain they could make a go of it.'

'So, you lent her the money? Six thousand pounds, you say?' A frown creased his brow. 'And now the money's disappeared?'

'That's right. The money—along with your brother. He suddenly seems to have vanished off the face of the earth ... Both Irene and I have tried writing and phoning, but the letters went unanswered, he's never in his office and and the phone at his flat just rings and rings.'

She paused and narrowed her eyes at him. 'And that's why I've come to see you ... So you can tell me where to find him.'

Axel shook his head at her. 'Well, that's quite a story. I must say I wasn't expecting to hear anything like this.'

'No doubt you find it shocking, just as I do.' Katrina looked into his face, searching for sympathy. 'No doubt you feel as I do that Jaime's behaved disgracefully and must be made to give the money back.'

When he said nothing, she frowned. 'Surely that's what you believe?'

Axel continued to say nothing for a few moments longer. Then he leaned forward and in a soft tone proceeded to enlighten her, 'I'll tell you exactly what I believe. I believe that what has happened is a tragedy. You're six thousand pounds down and I'm sure you don't deserve that. I'm not surprised to hear that you're shocked.

'But I've got news for you ...' He was starting to stand up now. 'News that I'm afraid you're not going to like. It wasn't my brother who stole that money from you. If anyone stole it, it was your sister. And I'm afraid it's your sister who's going to have to give it back. Though I suspect that's impossible. By now it's probably all been spent.'

'What are you saying? That's absolute nonsense!' Katrina leapt to her feet to face him. 'Why are you accusing my sister? Why are you defending

your brother? Don't you have any sense of
decency?'

'I think you ought to go now.' He was turning
away from her. 'It's very clear there's no way I can
help you.'

'Oh, but there is! You can tell me where your
brother is!' As he started to walk away from her
across the terrace, flushed with anger Katrina
hurried after him. 'You may be prepared to let your
brother get away with this, but I certainly am not,
so I'll deal with him myself.'

And that was when, shocking her into stillness,
Axel turned on her like a tiger.

'You will not go anywhere near my brother!
You'll stay away from him! You will make no effort
to contact him!' The black eyes blazed at her. 'Do
I make myself clear?'

'Very clear indeed. But you're wasting your
breath.'

Katrina's heart was pumping like a steam hammer
inside her. It was an effort to speak, an effort just
to look at him. His sudden anger was so fierce that
it electrified the air around them.

But Katrina was angry too now. Her green eyes
flashed defiantly. 'I'm going after your brother,
whatever you say, and I'm going to get that money
back!'

In that instant, like a whiplash, Axel had reached
out to catch hold of her, his fingers a vice around
her wrist. 'I'll say it one more time. Stay away from
my brother.' The strong tanned fingers bit into her
flesh, as he jerked her towards him and glared
into her face. 'Be warned. I'm not joking. Take
my advice.'

Katrina was paralysed for a moment, her feet glued to the paving stones, her senses overpowered by the virile black rage in him. Then she tossed her head at him. 'And if I don't?' she demanded.

'If you don't, you'll be sorry.' Unexpectedly, he released her. Then he turned on his heel and stormed back into the villa, pausing only to add in a snarl over his shoulder, 'You will be very sorry indeed, *señorita*.'

CHAPTER TWO

KATRINA was left to find her own way out of the villa. Axel had disappeared as though in a puff of smoke.

And good riddance, Katrina told herself, still shaking with fury, as she made her way down the gravel driveway to catch a taxi back to Santa Cruz and her hotel. Never in her life had she met such an odious man. *El diablo* was precisely what he was!

She frowned to herself. Irene had warned her what he was like, but quite frankly she had believed her sister was exaggerating. Now she knew the truth was the very opposite. He was even worse than the black picture her sister had painted!

Outside on the main road she stood for a few minutes, eyes squinting against the sun, searching for a taxi. But every one that passed was already taken. I'll walk, she decided. At least, for a bit. A good brisk walk might help to calm me down.

It was a little too hot, she soon discovered, for a good brisk walk—though an easy saunter proved equally refreshing. She glanced around her as she walked, at the tall waving palm trees and the bright blue sea beyond that seemed to stretch for ever, and she felt her spirits lift a little.

This was indeed paradise, she told herself, smiling. She rather envied her sister the year she had spent here.

And that was when, just as she was starting to calm down a bit, a long low gleaming black Mercedes whispered to a halt at the kerb beside her.

As the window slid down soundlessly and the passenger door was pushed open, the driver leaned across the seat towards her.

'Get in,' he told her.

It was Axel.

Hiding her surprise, Katrina looked right back at him. 'And why should I get in?' she enquired flatly.

'Because I ask you to.' He smiled a dark smile. 'And because,' he added, 'there's something more I want to say to you.'

'Oh, really? I'd got the impression that you were finished with me. The way you went storming off, I thought you'd said all you had to say.'

'Well, it would appear I haven't. So kindly get in.'

'Why? So you can have the pleasure of flinging more insults and more threats at me? No thanks. I've already had more than enough for one day.'

She had started to turn away, but then she stopped in her tracks as she heard him say, 'I'm sorry if I upset you. Perhaps I did go just a little over the top.'

Just for a moment Katrina was speechless. She blinked disbelievingly. Then she turned back to look at him. 'Was that really an apology? Surely I must be hearing things? I think I'm going to have to ask you to repeat it.'

He was watching her, half smiling, the dark eyes flickering with amusement. 'Don't push your luck,' he said. 'Just get in the car.'

As he spoke, he closed the window and slid back along the seat, leaving the passenger door standing open. Katrina hesitated for a moment. Was this wise? she wondered. She felt oddly nervous about climbing in beside him.

She heard a sigh of impatience. 'Well, what are you waiting for?'

Katrina wasn't really sure. Surely she had no reason to feel nervous? Even when she'd been at her most fiercely critical, Irene had never suggested he went in for kidnap or rape!

She was just being silly, Katrina decided. And, besides, she needed to co-operate with Axel if she was going to track down Jaime and get back the money.

Pushing aside her nervousness, she quickly climbed in.

Next minute she was sitting bolt upright in her seat, fearing that her initial nervous instincts had been right. 'Where are you taking me?' she squeaked. She'd expected him to take her back to the villa, but he was heading in entirely the opposite direction! 'I demand that you stop and let me out of here this minute!'

In response, Axel removed one hand from the steering-wheel and reached out towards her, making her jump back. He's about to attack me, she thought, suddenly touched by panic.

But he simply indicated her seatbelt. 'Kindly buckle up,' he said.

Katrina did as she was told, feeling slightly foolish. It seemed he was not about to attack her, after all. But still he hadn't answered her question.

She asked him again. 'Where are you taking me?'

'I'm going to show you something.'

'What?'

'Wait and see.' He turned to flash her a look of amusement. 'Don't worry, *señorita*, you're not being kidnapped.'

He clearly found her fears funny. Katrina tilted her chin at him. 'I only have your word for that.'

'My word is all you need. My word is my bond.'

'Just like your brother?'

She felt a little more in control again as she tossed the barb contemptuously across at him. And the scowl the remark instantly brought to his face simply made her feel even better.

They drove in silence for a few minutes, the big car heading towards Santa Cruz, Katrina trying to relax against the soft leather of the seat.

It looked as though he was taking her into the busy city—an unlikely kidnap destination!—but, although she no longer feared abduction, Katrina still felt tense and deeply uneasy. Oddly threatened. Almost claustrophobic. She had to keep thinking about her breathing.

It was his nearness that was doing it. His dark physical presence. And that, she realised abruptly, was what had made her nervous in the first place— the thought of climbing into a small, restricted space with him. It was the fear of physical closeness, not of being kidnapped, that had suddenly made her come out in goose-bumps!

Not that they were actually sitting all that close. The two front seats were huge and widely spaced. But she felt almost as though she were pressed up against him.

She could feel his warmth against her skin, making her flesh burn. The clean tangy scent of him filled her nostrils. And every time she stole a glance at the mahogany-dark arms or the splendid taut thighs encased in their slim blue trousers, she could actually feel their hard whiplash power as vividly as though she had reached out to touch him.

It was a shocking, frightening feeling, and she could not banish it. All she could do was breathe deeply and stare out of the window.

Then he spoke, making her jump. 'We're almost there. Now let's see if I can find a place to park.'

'Where are we?' It was ridiculous the way her heart was racing. Katrina forced herself to look at him. 'This is the town centre. What do you want to show me here?'

'Don't be so impatient. You'll know soon enough.' Axel flicked her one of his arrogant cool dark looks and, illogically, instantly, Katrina felt a little better. With that look a comforting distance had settled between them.

She breathed with relief and said, 'This had better be good.'

Axel parked in a narrow street, half across the pavement. Then he was climbing out, telling her, 'OK, we're here,' and next thing she was following him along the pavement to a big front door with a number 5 on it.

He pushed the door open, and, with Katrina at his heels, stepped into a narrow stone-flagged entrance hall. Then he was leading the way up a narrow winding staircase to another, smaller, front door and slipping a key from his pocket.

And that was when Katrina finally twigged. 'I know where we are!' she exclaimed, her hopes suddenly rising. 'This is Jaime's flat. Number five! This is where he and Irene stayed!'

'Well done. You're quite right.' Axel pushed the door open and stepped into a darkened hallway.

'Is he here?' Suddenly excited, Katrina hurried after him. 'I thought he was away. No one was answering the phone.'

But the flicker of hope in her was dying already. As, hard on Axel's heels, she stepped through an open doorway into what looked as though it had once been a sitting-room, she could see that the flat was completely empty. The phone that had rung unanswered every time she had tried calling sat bleakly in the middle of the dusty bare floorboards.

She turned angrily on Axel. 'Is this some kind of a joke? Why have you brought me here when the place is empty?'

'In order to save you time. I suspect you intended to come here anyway. Now you can see for yourself that there's absolutely no point.'

He was right, she had intended to come. And to keep coming again and again if at first she received no answer. She looked at him, hating him for the way he had second-guessed her. 'I hope you don't expect me to be grateful?' she said tightly.

'I don't expect anything.' His tone was cool and distant. 'Except perhaps that you finally understand that my brother's not here . . . and that you're not going to find him.'

'Oh, but I *am* going to find him. And perhaps I ought to thank you. I now know for sure that he's no longer here. And that's more than I knew a couple of minutes ago.'

'As I said, I've saved you time. You can now get on with your other business. And, once you've finished that, you can go back to Scotland.'

Katrina looked into his face as they stood there in the empty room, facing one another in the light from the window. His expression was hard and closed and forbidding. Hostility sprang from him like arrows from a bow.

'You seem very keen to get rid of me,' she observed. 'Well, that's a pity, because I won't be going until I find Jaime.'

'I see. You're planning an indefinite stay, are you?' His eyes surveyed her, as sharp as needles. 'That's what you seem to be suggesting?'

'Maybe I am.' But she blushed as she said it. Lies had never come easily to Katrina. She straightened her shoulders. 'I'll be staying until my job's done—but I'm sure that will provide me with enough time to find Jaime.'

Axel was standing very still, feet planted slightly apart, hands thrust into the pockets of his light blue trousers. He let a moment of silence pass, then he said, surprising her, 'That six thousand pounds you said you lent your sister... What on earth possessed you? It's a fair amount of money.'

'To me it is.' Though not to him, she suspected. Six thousand pounds to Axel Jerez was probably just loose change. 'That's one of the reasons I plan to get it back.'

He ignored that last bit. Still without moving, he put to her, 'I'm surprised a young woman like you has that sort of money to spare. They must pay very well in Scottish television.'

He was fishing. Very discreetly. But he was fishing. Katrina straightened her shoulders and narrowed her eyes at him. 'What's the matter? Don't you believe me? Do you think I'm lying about that loan to my sister?'

'I didn't say that. I just said it's a lot of money. I'm simply surprised that you have that sort of money to hand out.'

'Well, I don't any more. That was strictly a one-off. That was the last six thousand pounds in my account.'

'That makes it even more crazy of you to have given it to your sister. Don't you think so...considering your sister's character?'

'So, we're back to the insults?' Katrina glared at him. 'Well, I frankly don't care what you think of my sister's character. She may appear frivolous on the outside, but she's a good and decent girl, and I know she was keen to set up her own business.'

Axel laughed a scathing laugh. 'You're definitely crazy if you're telling me you seriously believe such a thing. Your sister's a lazy drop-out. She's not interested in making a living. All the time she was here she didn't hold down a job for more than a month.'

'That's not true. She worked at one of the hotels for longer than that!'

'OK, two months, then. But that was her limit. She's a waster. You should never have given her that money.'

'Well, I did, and I don't regret it.' As he stood there, hands in pockets, towering over her, dark

eyes burning into her, Katrina suddenly felt the need
to fold her arms across her chest. 'She knew she'd
been drifting in and out of jobs and she wasn't
happy with the situation. That was why she decided to do something about it. That was why she
asked me to lend her the money.'

'And, just like that, you handed it over. Your
last six thousand pounds. Wow! That was real
madness.'

He was still standing very still, straight-backed,
hands in pockets, but that earlier harsh look in his
eyes had vanished. He smiled and allowed the smile
to linger, his eyes drifting over her, thoughtfully,
unhurriedly.

'As I said before, what on earth possessed you?'

'Irene needed the money.' Katrina wanted to step
away from him. Suddenly she was finding it difficult to breathe again, just as she had earlier in
the car. 'I felt it was my duty to help her out.'

'Your duty?'

'Yes, sort of...'

She had been about to enlarge on that, but at
that very instant he slipped one hand from his
pocket and reached out to lift a curl of hair from
her shoulder.

'You know, I wasn't joking when I said I was
partial to redheads. And you, my dear Katrina, have
the reddest hair I've ever seen.'

Katrina's mouth had gone as dry as the dusty
floorboards she stood on. From the corner of her
eye she could see his long tanned fingers around
which curled a strand of her long red hair. She
licked her parched lips as her heart broke into
a gallop.

'All of the MacGregors have red hair,' she said.

'Yes, you said you got it from your father.' He twisted his fingers around the curling strand, and, though it was really a very tiny movement, Katrina felt her scalp burst into flames. Suddenly, every inch of her seemed to be trembling.

He smiled. 'Does your father, who has given you this priceless inheritance...' Again, softly, he twisted the strand of hair around his fingers. 'Does he know you so unwisely lent this money to your sister?'

'Of course he knows.' Her voice sounded husky. She quickly cleared her throat. 'Yes. Of course.'

'You mean you tell your father everything?'

'Not everything. Of course not.'

She dared not look into his eyes. If she did, they would swallow her. So she stared fixedly at his chin and for the first time noticed, there, among the jet-black bristles of his beard, a pale jagged scar about a centimetre long.

Keeping her eyes fixed on it, as though it were her lifeline, she elaborated, 'But I happen to be very close to both my parents. Naturally, I would tell them something like that.'

'And they approved of the gesture?'

'Of course. Why shouldn't they? They'd have lent it themselves if they'd had it to spare.'

'But they didn't have it to spare?'

'No, they don't have much money.'

'And so your sister came with her begging bowl to you?'

The harsh reference to Irene caused Katrina to glance up at him, but instantly she flicked her gaze back to the scar again. She'd been right, those eyes

of his would swallow her. She cleared her throat
again. 'Yes, I suppose so.'

'And just like that, without a second thought,
you dropped your last six thousand pounds into
it...?'

What was he getting at? Her gaze strayed up to
his eyes again. But, even as her heart jolted at the
smoky dark look there, he did something that
whipped the ground from under her feet.

Unhurriedly, he lifted the strand of bright red
hair and softly stroked it along her jawline. Then,
shaking his head, a teasing look in his eyes, he
gently brushed the end of her nose with it. 'You
crazy, crazy girl,' he said.

It was as though a bolt of lightning had shot right
through her, sending flames jumping out of her,
nailing her to the floor. Katrina was struggling for
breath as he released the strand of hair and slipped
his hand back into his trouser pocket.

She said, feeling she was drowning, fighting to
stay afloat, desperate to shake the feeling from her,
'As I said, in a way I felt it was my duty.'

'How so?' He had stepped back, so that he was
standing by the window. A shaft of sunlight hit his
shoulder and lit up his dark hair—but now, to
Katrina's relief, his eyes were in shadow. 'Why on
earth did you think it was your duty?'

'It was an inheritance, you see. Or, at least, a
part of an inheritance.'

As she said the word inheritance again she remembered how he had described her hair as an inheritance from her father. And, thinking of her
hair, she felt her scalp burn again, as though the

long tanned fingers were still hovering above her shoulder, laced among the bright red curls.

She hurried on, 'An aunt of ours died a few months ago. She left me some money—fourteen thousand pounds. I'd spent most of it on having my roof fixed and central heating installed, but there was six thousand pounds left when Irene approached me about the loan...' Her voice trailed off. 'So, you see, I could hardly refuse.'

'No, I don't see, I'm afraid. Tell me. Why couldn't you refuse?'

'Well, I'd been left all that money and Irene'd been left nothing. Somehow it didn't seem fair. I was glad to share it with her.'

She was telling him all this needlessly. It was really none of his business. A voice at the back of her head was telling her that, but somehow she couldn't stop the words pouring out of her. The fact was, she found the sound of her own voice reassuring. It proved that, at least vocally, she was still functioning!

Axel shifted his weight slightly against the window-frame, and though his eyes were still in shadow Katrina could feel them pierce through her.

'Presumably,' he put to her, 'your aunt left you the money because she wanted you, and not your sister, to have it.'

'Oh, I don't think that... I mean, that she had anything against Irene. It's just that I was closer to her than Irene. I was her god-daughter, you see, and I think she thought of me as her real daughter. She had no children of her own.'

'As I said, she wanted you and not your sister
to have the money. To me she sounds like a most
sensible woman.'

'She was a lovely woman. I was very fond of her.'

'And she, quite clearly, was very fond of you.'
Axel paused and the shadowed eyes for a moment
bored into her. Then he said, 'Why do you feel the
need to heap handouts on your sister?'

'I don't feel the need to heap handouts on her.'

'It looks that way to me.'

'I just want to help her.'

'Why?'

'Because she's my sister and because she's
younger than me. Nearly five years younger. Irene's
only twenty, you know. She's just a kid.'

Axel smiled at that. She saw a flash of white
teeth. 'I'll bet you were saying the same thing when
you were twenty, and you'll be saying the same thing
when you're fifty, no doubt. She'll always be
younger than you, and she'll always be just a kid
to you. Though I'll bet you weren't a kid when you
were twenty.'

I couldn't afford to be. Katrina almost said it.
But she stopped herself in time. It was none of
Axel's business. She'd been just twenty when her
father's business had gone bust and her mother,
from the shock, had almost fallen apart. During
that time she'd grown up fast. She'd held the family
together. Her father had told her that often. She'd
been the strong one.

And it had become a habit, especially with Irene.
For Irene was like her mother, over-sensitive and
highly strung.

.

She narrowed her eyes now at Axel, remembering what Irene had told her. 'I understand you don't suffer from the same affliction—the need to heap handouts on a younger sibling?'

According to Irene, while Axel lived in luxury, Jaime, who held a very minor position in one of his companies, was literally always counting the pennies. 'It would never have occurred to you to help your brother set himself up in business.'

'This proposed shop of theirs, you mean?' Axel shook his head. 'For a start, I can assure you it never existed... But, anyway, you're right, I wouldn't have helped.'

'Well, at least you're honest.' Katrina raised a surprised eyebrow. She hadn't expected such unaffected bluntness, though she had known the truth. Irene had told her that Axel had refused Jaime financial help many times in the past.

'I suppose you believe everyone should make their own way in the world, as you did?'

That was something else Irene had told her—that he'd risen, entirely by his own efforts, from being the son of a penniless Spanish shopkeeper to a multi-millionaire before he was thirty.

'No one helped you,' she added, 'so you don't help anyone in return?' He had two married brothers and a sister besides Jaime, and she suspected he didn't help any of them either.

He shifted slightly and suddenly she could see his eyes again. They were smiling an amused, uncaring smile. 'That sounds like a reasonable philosophy to me.'

'Does it? I would say it was a little heartless. Not everyone's as able as you are, after all.'

'You're right, they're not.' He accepted the compliment with a small nod, making her wish she hadn't said it. 'Nor,' he added, 'is everyone prepared to work as hard as I've done.' Then he surprised her. 'Nor as hard as you've done, I suspect.'

He held her eyes. 'I'll bet when you were twenty you weren't bumming around the Canaries doing odd jobs, like your sister?'

That was true; she had been at university when she was twenty, studying as hard as she could for the best degree she could get.

'Irene's different,' she defended. 'Not everyone's the same. Anyway, her bumming around the Canaries was only a phase. As I told you, she wanted to to set up her own business.'

'Wanted? Past tense. You mean she's changed her mind again?'

'She didn't have much choice. She hasn't got any money now. Your brother, as I keep telling you, took it and disappeared.' But it was true, Katrina thought privately. Irene had changed her mind.

Axel shrugged, almost as though he had read her private thoughts. 'Then she doesn't need the money if she's not going into business.'

'Yes, she does. She needs it for something else.'

'Something else. Yes, that sounds typical. And next month it'll be something else again.' With a shake of his head, he detached himself from the window-frame and folded his arms across his chest. 'Why don't you just accept that your sister's a lost cause and go back to Scotland and start thinking about yourself?'

'Maybe because I'm not like you.' Suddenly, Katrina was angry. Who did he think he was telling her what she ought to do? 'My sister needs that money and I intend to get it back for her—and I object to the way you just casually shrug it off, as though six thousand pounds was a mere drop in the ocean.'

'It may as well have been dropped in the ocean for all the hope you have of ever seeing it again.' He smiled a cruel smile as he stepped towards her. 'Why don't you just accept that? Your money is gone.'

'Why? Because you refuse to help me? Because you refuse to tell me where I can find your brother?' Katrina glanced round the empty room with a sudden dart of frustration. 'I suppose you brought me here, just so you could gloat? Well, you can gloat if you like, but I'll find him in spite of you!'

Axel stepped in front of her then and took hold of her by the shoulders. 'You're on the wrong track. That's what I'm trying to tell you. There were never any business plans and my brother didn't take the money. So, it's totally pointless you trying to track him down.'

'I don't believe you.' Katrina tried to pull away from him, but his fingers dug into her flesh like vices. 'You're just covering up. Jaime did take the money. My sister wouldn't lie to me about a thing like that!'

'Such misguided faith.' Axel shook his head. 'Your sister would lie to you about anything, and she has. Take my word for it, I know that for a fact.'

'And what is that supposed to mean? What has she lied about? Go on, tell me. Give me the proof!'

He seemed to hesitate for a moment as a dark
look touched his eyes. 'It would be so easy,' he said.
For a moment he held his breath.

Then he released her and stepped away. 'Look,'
he told her. 'I know my brother doesn't have that
money. I don't know what happened to it, but my
guess is it's all been spent ... on nightclubs and
clothes and wining and dining ... That was the way
your sister and Jaime lived and it wouldn't be hard
to get through six thousand pounds. Believe me,
that's what I'm sure has happened.'

'But I don't believe you.' Katrina was adamant.
'You may find this strange, but I believe my sister.
I believe what she told me, that your brother took
the money.'

'Then you really are a fool.' The dark eyes narrowed as he looked at her. 'Take my word for it,
your sister's a liar.'

'So you keep saying, but I'm still waiting for
proof.' Katrina looked into his face. 'You were
about to tell me something. Something you implied
would prove that she'd lied. So tell me now,' she
challenged. 'I'm listening.'

But he was turning away. 'I've had enough of
this. Let's get out of here.' He headed for the door.

'Not until you've told me!'

Katrina tried to block the way. But he simply
steered her ahead of him out through the front
door.

Axel slammed the door behind him. 'Forget it,'
he growled.

'No, I won't forget it! You were about to tell me
something. You can't just start to tell something
and then change your mind!'

He was hurrying down the steps while she hurried behind him. 'You're wrong, I'm afraid. That's precisely what I'm going to do.'

'No, you won't. I won't let you. I demand that you tell me. If you're going to call Irene a liar, then you ought to prove it!'

'As I said, it would be so easy.'

'OK, then do it!'

'Not for the moment.'

As he reached the main door, Axel stopped in his tracks and turned round suddenly to face her. And there was nothing Katrina could do. She went slamming straight into him.

It was only for a brief moment that their two bodies came together. As soon as they made contact, Katrina was jumping away, almost tripping and falling in her confusion.

But in that brief moment, as she was thrown against his chest and felt his strength and caught the cool subtle scent of him, she was seized by an uncontrollable *frisson* of excitement. Never before had she been so deliciously aware of another body.

The reaction was so powerful that, for a moment, it threw her. She felt herself freeze with horror as she stared into his face.

'Are you OK?'

Responding to her stunned expression, Axel had reached out a steadying hand towards her.

'Yes, I'm fine. Just winded.'

But he did not actually touch her. It was as though he'd sensed the tension in her and realised she'd jump through the roof if he did. He just stood there looking at her, his expression strange.

'I'm sorry. I didn't mean to bump into you like that.'

'It's OK. I'm OK.'

Her heart was still beating wildly. She was having difficulty tearing her gaze away from him. Why doesn't he just open the door and step outside? she wondered desperately. Locked with him like this in the small, dark hallway, she was starting to feel claustrophobic again.

But he made no move to open the door. Instead, he stepped closer, so that he was standing directly over her.

'A reminder,' he growled. 'While I have your full attention.' He reached out arrogantly and brushed her hair with his fingers. 'Don't go against me. I wouldn't like that. Just be a good girl and do as I say.'

He held her eyes for a moment, his expression dark and dangerous, causing her already racing heart to race faster. And suddenly she was wondering what he was meaning. What exactly was it he was asking her to do?

Then, even as she stood there in a state of confusion, he turned round abruptly and flung the door open.

In that moment, as bright sunlight poured in through the narrow doorway, the tension in Katrina abruptly slackened. Suddenly, with the darkness the sense of danger had flown.

Her eyes flicked to Axel's profile that was caught in the doorway. 'Don't try to threaten me,' she told him.

He ignored this rebuke and stepped out on to the pavement. Then, as she was about to follow him, he turned to her and demanded, 'How long will your business with Fergus Loughlin take?' He paused. 'I take it that is who you've come to see? Fergus Loughlin, the eminent Scottish sculptor, who is also one of the island's most famous residents.'

Of course, he was right and his cleverness was grating. Katrina responded with irritation. 'Several days. Perhaps a week.' Then as the dark eyes glinted with unconcealed displeasure, she added, 'Who knows? Perhaps even longer.'

There was another glint of displeasure. 'Why so long?' he wanted to know.

Katrina shrugged. 'When the team come to do the interview proper, they'll want to speak to other people besides Loughlin—friends of his... people who know him... So it's my job to dig out the most interesting ones and get them to agree to take part in the programme. And of course I'll also have to look for suitable locations where all these various interviews can be filmed.'

'I see.' Axel was looking more and more displeased. His expression had grown as black as thunder. 'I hadn't realised,' he growled. 'I thought your stay here would be brief. A matter of a couple of days at the most.'

'Then I'm sorry to disappoint you.'

'Oh, don't be sorry just yet.' He fixed her with a dark look. 'Let's not be premature. After all, I haven't been disappointed yet.'

'And what is that supposed to mean?'

But he ignored her and turned away. 'Let's go. I'll give you a lift back to your hotel.'

'Don't bother. I'll walk.'

Katrina remained standing in the doorway. She had quite recovered now from their unsettling collision, but all the same just the thought of climbing into the car with him was suddenly bringing her out in her goose-bumps.

Axel could not have cared less whether she chose to join him or not. 'As you please,' he told her and headed for the car.

It was a relief to see him go, but he still hadn't answered her question.

She called after him, 'What was that last remark supposed to mean? That remark about you not being disappointed yet?' Then, as he continued to ignore her, she added angrily to his retreating back, 'You *will* be disappointed! I'll be here for quite a while. And the fact that you don't like it is just too bad!'

He had reached the car and was pulling open the driver's door. 'You think so? We'll see about that,' he growled.

But it was not the warning in his voice that caused Katrina to shiver and step back abruptly in the doorway. It was the way he'd turned to look at her as he'd said it, drawing her with his eyes so that, just for a moment, she was pressed up against him again, alight with excitement, in the hallway.

CHAPTER THREE

AFTER that unsettling parting from Axel, Katrina walked back to her hotel, quietly fuming.

She was partly fuming at herself for reacting to him so foolishly, but for the most part her fuming was directed at him.

Who did he think he was, trying to threaten her like that? Well, he could threaten all he liked. It made no difference. She would stay as long as she needed to and, what was more, she'd find Jaime!

She showered and changed and had a light lunch. Then, armed with the list of names that Irene had given her, she set off on the trail of Axel's missing brother.

'These are some of our friends, the people we used to mix with. If Axel won't tell you where he is,' Irene had assured her, 'someone on that list is bound to be able to help you.'

Sadly, however, that was not how it turned out.

The first name on the list was the owner of a small garage. He shrugged at Katrina. 'I haven't seen Jaime for days.'

'But you must know where he's living,' Katrina insisted. 'Don't you even have a phone number? Anything would do.'

But the young man just shrugged again. 'Sorry, I don't know anything.' Then he simply turned his back on her. 'I've got to get back to work.'

The story was more or less the same with every name on the list. It seemed that not a single one of his acquaintances had any idea where Jaime was.

Or else they did know, but just weren't telling.

Once more back at the hotel, Katrina sat out on her little balcony with a pot of her favourite Earl Grey tea. It just wasn't possible that nobody knew anything. More likely what she'd run into was an elaborate and efficient cover-up. Jaime didn't want to be found and had sworn his friends to silence.

Katrina sighed and gazed out at the breathtaking panorama that was spread out in magical colours before her, the bright green of the palm trees, the blazing red of bougainvillaea, the dancing, sparkling blue of the sea. Poor Irene, she thought, to have lost all this.

She felt a hot flare of anger against the faithless Jaime. In spite of all the slurs Axel had cast at her head, Irene had been deeply in love with Jaime.

Katrina remembered the glowing letters of the early days of the romance when Irene had made the decision to stay on in Tenerife. 'I have to be here to be with Jaime,' she'd written. 'And, anyway, I love the island almost as much as I love him.'

That was easy to understand, Katrina thought now, smiling. It would be exceedingly easy to fall in love with Tenerife. As to Jaime, however, she had no way of judging. She knew him only from the photographs Irene had sent her—wonderfully happy, laughing photographs of the two of them together.

For a moment, as she gazed seawards, her memory focused on these photographs. She remembered a slim young man with clean-cut features, handsome enough, but in no way memorable. In that respect he differed totally from his older brother.

An image of Axel flashed before her brain, causing an unexpected, and unwelcome, start within her. His younger brother—at twenty-five, younger by nine years—had none of his powerful physique and extraordinary presence. Even from a mere photograph that was obvious. The two brothers were as different as chalk and cheese.

Well, perhaps not so different, really, under the skin, Katrina found herself amending. Both of them, she suspected, were shameless philanderers. And though she had no reason to believe Axel was a thief like his brother, the way he was defending Jaime was almost as bad.

Katrina sighed and thought again of her heartbroken sister who had fled back to Scotland and the sanctuary of their parents' home after Jaime had disappeared off with his new girlfriend and the money. And her blood boiled with anger at the sheer cynical callousness of any man who would sink to such despicable behaviour—and the equally cynical callousness of the brother who would defend him.

She started to pour more tea, but the teapot was empty. She laid it down with a sigh and drained the cold dregs in her cup. Axel had said he didn't believe that his brother had taken the money. He'd insisted that Jaime and Irene had blown it having a good time. But that was sheer nonsense. A malicious invention. Axel Jerez was as big a blackguard as his brother.

Katrina stood up and stared out to sea for a moment, a tall slender figure in a blue cotton robe, her mane of red hair falling halfway to her waist in a tumbling riot of soft, bright curls. I'll beat them both, she told herself firmly. In spite of Axel, I shall find his rotten brother and return to Scotland with the money!

Strengthened by that thought, she glanced at her watch—and saw that it was time she started getting herself ready. An hour from now she had an appointment with Fergus Loughlin.

She smiled to herself, her spirits lifting. So far, it had been a maddeningly frustrating day when absolutely nothing had gone her way. But now she had the chance to end it on a high note. Surely nothing could go wrong in her meeting with Loughlin?

Forty minutes later Katrina was climbing into a taxi and heading down the coast road to where the sculptor had his villa. Seven o'clock, he had said. She was going to be bang on time.

Her spirts were high. She was looking forward to this meeting. She had enormous admiration for Fergus Loughlin's work and it would be wonderful finally to meet the man in person.

She had just one moment of unease before they reached the sprawling villa, though with a determined toss of her head Katrina dismissed it. On this island there were probably scores of black Mercedeses. Such cars were probably ten a penny. So it meant nothing that, just as they turned off the main road and headed up the side road that led to Loughlin's villa, a sleek black Mercedes, the image of Axel's, whisked past them, heading in the opposite direction.

Don't be silly, she told herself, as her heart faltered inside her.

But five minutes later, she was feeling far less certain. In response to her knock, a housekeeper answered. 'I'm sorry,' Katrina was told, 'Mr Loughlin's not available.' And with that the door began to close.

'But I have an appointment. Mr Loughlin's expecting me. Please tell him it's Katrina MacGregor. I'm sure you're mistaken.'

But the woman was adamant. 'I'm sorry. He's not available.' A moment later the door closed firmly in Katrina's face.

That was bad enough, but there was even worse to come.

Next morning she was awakened by the delivery of a letter. She tore it open and read the contents and felt her insides turn to powder.

I regret I am no longer agreeable to taking part in your TV programme. I apologise for any inconvenience. Yours sincerely, Fergus Loughlin.

Katrina stared for a stunned moment or two at the brief scrawled message. Then she tossed it aside angrily, squared her shoulders and firmed her jaw.

'Axel Jerez,' she muttered, 'I want some explanations!'

'I don't care if he's in a meeting! I demand to see him this instant!'

In the same breath Katrina was striding past the startled secretary and flinging open the door behind the girl's desk.

'I'm afraid this is urgent. I can't wait any longer!' The next moment she was bursting into the office beyond.

It was a huge room with a huge window through which poured bright sunlight that caused Katrina to pause and blink for a moment.

Then a voice spoke. Axel's voice.

'If I may say so, that was quite an entrance. Now I would be grateful if you would make an equally stunning exit.'

In response Katrina took a further couple of steps into the room, still squinting against the bright sunlight from the window. But as her eyes rapidly adjusted she could make out a huge desk, behind which was seated the dark-suited figure of a furious-looking, tight-lipped Axel Jerez.

She glared at him. 'Your secretary said you were in a meeting. I can't see any meeting. There's nobody here but you.'

'And you, it would now appear. One too many.' He half rose in his seat. 'Once again, I invite you leave.'

'I have no intention of leaving.' Katrina flicked a glance round her, searching for a chair in which to park herself. There was one just to her right, button-backed, in green leather. She plonked herself down in it in a hurry, like someone playing musical chairs. 'I won't leave until you've told me what the devil's going on.'

'What's going on, it seems to me, is that you have barged into my office when I expressly forbade you entry...'

'You didn't forbid me entry.' Katrina clutched the chair arms. He had risen fully to his feet now and was fixing her across the desk, an acre of elegant polished mahogany, with eyes as merciless as a pair of bayonets. 'You got your secretary to lie and tell me you were in a meeting.'

'It boils down to the same thing.' His eyes flashed in the sunlight. 'I made it clear that I had no intention of seeing you.'

'So, you intended to leave me sitting out there all day? As it is, I've already been waiting for more than an hour!'

'How unfortunate.' Then he smiled a slow sadistic smile. 'Well, at least it kept you out of mischief.'

Katrina understood at once. 'You mean looking for your brother?' Her green eyes flashed. 'Well, you could have saved yourself the trouble. It's not your brother who's on my mind right now. It's Fergus Loughlin—and you!'

'Is that a fact?'

He was moving round his desk, soundlessly, like a big cat closing in on its prey. Katrina was suddenly wishing she weren't sitting. He loomed over her, a dark and threatening presence. Just for a moment her heartbeat quickened as she found herself back in that narrow, darkened hallway.

Then he paused on the nearside of the desk, leaned against it lightly and glanced towards the door through which Katrina had made her entrance.

'*Esta bien*,' he said softly, addressing the secretary, who still stood, wide-eyed and apologetic in the doorway. Then as the door clicked shut, he fixed his gaze on Katrina. 'So, now we are alone,' he said.

Katrina shifted in her seat as something stirred within her at the way the dark eyes seemed to reach out and touch her. She felt again the impact of his hard body against her own and an accompanying thrust of quick excitement. Just for a moment she felt warm from head to toe.

But she squashed these feelings instantly and straightened her shoulders. 'Yes, we are,' she responded, as though it were a mere detail. 'And now I would be grateful if you would oblige me by answering some questions.'

One black eyebrow lifted. 'And what makes you think for one minute that I have any intention of answering your questions?'

'Because I don't intend moving from here until you do. And though you may have been quite happy to keep me sitting in your outer office all day, I doubt you'd feel the same about me sitting in here.'

'I won't argue with that.' Axel raised his head and looked at her, as though he were studying her in detail. 'But take my word for it, *señorita*,' he told her, 'it would be a simple matter for me to eject you.'

'You'd have to use force.'

'No doubt I would. But I think I'd manage.'

He paused and continued his careful scrutiny, his eyes drifting over her from the top of her burnished head, down the length of her shapely body in its flattering green dress, to her neat slim feet in their cream-coloured sandals.

'After all, what do you weigh? No more than fifty-five kilos, or eight and half stone in English weight.' As she flushed, he added, 'I think I'm quite capable of shifting fifty-five kilos out of my office.'

He made a sudden movement. 'What do you think?'

Katrina had started at the sudden movement, as no doubt he had intended, for now he was smiling a light, amused smile.

He held her eyes a moment. 'Do you wish to put me to the test?'

'No, I do not.'

Though it was an effort to do so, Katrina forced herself to hold her gaze absolutely steady. For, all at once, her stomach was churning like a cement mixer and her skin seemed to tingle where his eyes had touched her. And again she felt touched by the sense of sheer excitement that she'd felt when they'd collided in that darkened hallway.

It's pure sex, she thought with horror, as she continued to hold his gaze. Just the thought of physical contact with him and I'm up in flames. And it was disgraceful. She made a mental note to curb the reaction.

Controlling herself carefully, she told him half sceptically, 'Surely you're not the sort of man who would use physical force against a helpless female?'

He laughed then, though not the brief sharp bark of yesterday, but a full-throated laugh that brought a smile to Katrina's own lips.

'So, you're helpless, are you? Frankly, I would never have thought it. Still, how can I resist such an appeal to my better nature?'

'So, you have one, after all?'

'A better nature?' He smiled again. 'Some would say not. And—who knows?—maybe they're right. I'll leave you to judge that for yourself.'

Axel straightened suddenly and leaned across the desk towards her. 'So, now that you've forced yourself into my presence, I suppose you may as well tell me the purpose of your visit.'

'I think you already know that.'

'If I did, I would not be asking.' With a flash of impatience he sat back in his seat again. 'It is not my habit to waste time with pointless questions.'

He was bluffing, of course. But then he was good at bluffing. 'OK.' Katrina met his gaze over the desk top. 'Since you say you don't know, let me tell you why I'm here.' She paused. 'Yesterday afternoon you made a veiled threat...' She narrowed her eyes at him. 'Do you remember?'

His gaze never flickered. 'I can't say I do. What was the nature of this veiled threat of mine?'

'It was when I told you I would need to stay on the island for some time—a revelation which quite obviously didn't please you... You said, and I remember clearly... You said, "We'll see about that".'

'Did I, indeed? And what do you suppose I meant?'

'I had no idea at the time.' His coolness was maddening. Not the ghost of a giveaway flicker had touched the dark eyes. Katrina's fists clenched with annoyance as she leaned towards him. 'But now, of course, I do,' she said.

'Then kindly enlighten me.'

He had laid one hand on the desk edge, and against the band of crisp white shirt-cuff that jutted

below the cuff of his jacket his wrist looked sinuous
and deeply tanned.

He has elegant hands, Katrina found herself
thinking—a thought which clashed somewhat with
the antagonistic mood of the moment.

She snatched her eyes from his hand and focused
on his face, which with its current arrogant expression was more conducive to antagonism. 'Let
me tell you the whole story...' She crossed her feet
at the ankles and smoothed the skirt of her dress
over her knees. 'Yesterday evening I had an appointment with Fergus Loughlin... And guess
what?'

'I've no idea.'

'He wasn't available.'

'That was unfortunate for you.'

'Most unfortunate.' Still not a shadow of guilt
had touched his face. He really was a shameless
trickster. 'And then this morning,' she continued,
'I received a note telling me——'

'A note from whom?' Axel interrupted, for all
the world as though he really didn't know. Katrina's
sense of wonderment at his duplicity shot up
another notch.

She shook her head at him. 'Fergus Loughlin,
of course.' As though it actually needed saying!
'Telling me he's changed his mind about the programme. He's no longer prepared to take part in
it, it seems.'

There was a moment of silence, during which
Axel reached for a silver paperclip that had been
lying on the spotless white blotter in front of him.
He toyed with it idly as he said, without glancing

at her, 'That would seem to make it rather pointless for you to stay on in Tenerife.'

'Funny, I thought you'd say that.' Katrina straightened and glared at him, her anger seething like a cauldron. 'In fact, that is precisely what I thought you'd say.'

'So, it has occurred to you also?' He flicked a cruel smile across at her. 'Well, I suppose it's bound to have, after all. It must be plain to anyone that it's pointless you staying on.'

The anger in her was making it difficult for her to breathe. Katrina clenched her fists tightly, wishing she could strangle him. She said, 'You did this, didn't you? You set this up. You're the one who made him change his mind!'

'Me?' He had the gall to feign innocence for a moment. He tossed the paperclip and neatly caught it. 'Why are you blaming me for your problems?'

'Because of that threat you made. That ''we'll see about that''.' Then, as he seemed about to shake his head, she added, 'And because I saw you leaving Loughlin's place last night.'

He had not expected that. He became very still for a moment, watching her from beneath twin curtains of long black lashes. Then he shrugged. 'I might have been there for any number of reasons.'

Katrina had known, of course, that he was guilty, but that shameless virtual confession sent an icy shiver through her. He's monstrous, she thought. How could he do this to me, then sit there, un-repentant, and look me in the face?

'I suppose you could have been,' she consented. 'But we both know you weren't.'

Axel continued, unblinkingly, to watch her across the desktop. Then he raised one dark eyebrow. 'So, how soon do you leave?'

The question shocked her. And, again, she thought, he's monstrous. 'How could you do this?' she demanded tightly. 'It's vicious. You're playing around with my job.'

Still, he appeared unconcerned. 'Will they fire you?' he enquired equably.

'Fire me? For what?' She looked him straight in the eye.

He looked straight back at her. 'For failing to do your job.'

'And who said I'm going to fail?' Katrina's heart was thumping with anger. 'You may have succeeded in thwarting me for the moment, but I'll get my interview and the programme will go ahead. I'll get hold of Loughlin and change his mind back again.' She narrowed her green eyes at him. 'Just you wait and see!'

'You sound very certain.' Axel's tone was sceptical as he tossed the silver paperclip and caught it again. 'But perhaps you ought to consider the possibility that you might fail.'

'I won't fail.' Katrina's tone was tight with determination. 'I've never failed to do my job properly in the past, and I don't intend to start failing now.'

'An admirable attitude.' Axel raised one dark eyebrow and glanced down at the silver paperclip in his hand. 'However,' he observed, 'there's a first time for everything. And that includes failing to do one's job properly.'

Then with a sudden callous smile he flicked the silver paperclip in the direction of the pen holder that stood behind the blotter. 'Bullseye!' he congratulated himself as it dropped straight in.

Katrina gritted her teeth, controlling her surging anger. 'I won't fail,' she muttered in a grim, tight voice.

There was a moment of silence as the dark eyes swept over her. Then Axel put to her, his tone amused and dismissive, 'So, what are you doing here if you still have a job to do? Why aren't you out there, tracking Loughlin down?'

'You're right, I ought to be. I'm wasting my time here.' With a disdainful glance at him, Katrina rose to her feet. 'But, you see, I had the silly notion that I might be able to persuade you to stop working against me, to talk to Loughlin again and undo the damage that you've temporarily done.'

She laughed a hollow laugh. 'Of course, I can see now how silly that was. You're prepared to do anything to try and force me to leave the island. And all in order to keep me from your brother.'

'I'm glad you're remembering that I've advised you to stay away from him.' The dark eyes glinted a warning as he spoke.

'Oh, I'm remembering, all right...' Katrina met his gaze pointedly. 'But I've no intention of accommodating you on that score either. Not only will I pursue my interview with Loughlin...I'll also track down your brother and get back Irene's money!'

'And how long do you expect all of this to take you?' As he spoke, Axel was rising to his feet. 'So far you've been rather vague about that.'

Yes, she had been. Deliberately. In order to needle him. But the plain fact was that she'd been given ten days to set up the interviews for the programme. If she twisted his arm, her boss might stretch it to two weeks. But as her expression clearly showed, her time here was strictly limited. And her first priority was to do the job she'd come for.

At that thought she experienced a flash of understanding. 'I know what you're up to,' she proceeded to accuse Axel. 'You're making things difficult for me with Loughlin so I won't have time to try and find Jaime. Well, it won't work,' she told him. 'I'll find Jaime in spite of you. I'll stay on after my job's done at my own expense.'

'If you can find a hotel room. At this time of year they're all booked up.'

'I'll sleep on a park bench!'

'I wouldn't advise that.'

As he smiled at her callously, knowing she was bluffing, Katrina was almost choking with frustration. There was no way she could afford to stay on at her own expense. Once she'd finished with Loughlin, she'd definitely have to leave.

But, as she stood there fuming, Axel was stepping towards her, and all at once his expression seemed to have softened.

'Why are you making it so hard for yourself?' he asked her, standing over her and fixing her with those eyes as black as midnight. 'Why not just accept the fact that you're beaten, catch the first plane home and forget about all this? Your meeting with Loughlin's off, you're not going to find Jaime, and there's no six thousand pounds for you to get back.'

'My meeting with Loughlin's not off. That you can count on. And I will find Jaime. And the money.'

The dark eyes looked down at her and there was no hardness in them at all now. Instead, from their inky depths shone a look almost of compassion.

Then he sighed. 'Look, I was planning to come by your hotel later... What I wanted to do was give you this...'

His eyes never leaving hers, he reached into his inside pocket and drew out a folded piece of paper. 'Take it,' he said, handing it to her, 'and just go back home.'

A little thrown by the sudden, unexpected change in him, Katrina took the piece of paper. 'What is it?' she asked him. That softness in his eyes was making her heart wobble. She could feel the breath catch at the back of her throat.

He smiled at her, a smile that made her blood rush. Suddenly, ridiculously, she was tingling from head to foot.

'It's yours. It's what you came for,' he told her.

'What I came for?'

With difficulty, Katrina unlocked her eyes from his that seemed to be drawing her down like whirlpools. She unfolded the piece of paper and forced herself to focus on it.

A moment later her eyes were springing wide open with astonishment. 'Good grief. What's this?' She looked up into Axel's face again. 'This is a cheque for six thousand pounds!'

'Yes, and it's yours.'

'You mean it's *my* six thousand pounds? But it's signed by you! Did Jaime give you the money?'

Axel did not answer. He took hold of her hand and gently folded her fingers round the cheque. 'Just take it and go,' he said, closing his own hand over hers. 'Consider the matter finished. This is the money you lost.'

'But it's not!' Katrina frowned into his face in confusion. 'This isn't my six thousand pounds. This didn't come from Jaime. Did it?' she insisted. 'This money's from you!'

'What's the difference? It's still six thousand pounds. It's what you came for and now you've got it.' His hand was still clasped around her fingers, forcing her to hold on to the cheque. His eyes bored into her. 'So, just take it and go.'

'But I don't want your money! What are you saying? I can't possibly take this from you!' With sudden strength, Katrina snatched her hand free and thrust the cheque at him as though it were contaminated. 'I don't want your money. I just want Irene's money back!'

'What difference does it make?' As she sprang away from him, Axel caught hold of her, his dark eyes almost beseeching, ignoring the cheque which now fluttered to the floor. 'Look, you deserve to have your money back. Take it. I don't want you to be out of pocket.'

Katrina felt quite shell-shocked. Her head was spinning. 'You're only offering me the money because you want rid of me! Because you don't want me tracking down your brother!' She stepped away from him. 'What's going on?' she demanded. 'Why are you so desperate to keep me from your brother?'

He did not answer that. 'And what about you, *señorita*? Why are you acting so ridiculously proud?

I've offered to give you what you came for. Don't you think it's a little crazy just to reject it out of hand?'

'No, I don't! Perhaps I am ridiculously proud! Too proud, at any rate, to accept handouts from you. It's my money—Irene's money—I want, not yours!'

'Well, I'm afraid my money is the only money you're going to get, so I really would advise you to take it.' He frowned down at her. 'Look, if you take the money and agree to be gone from here within forty-eight hours, I'll get Loughlin to do the interview after all. Then you'll have everything you want.'

'I won't take it. It's a bribe and I won't be bribed! I can get Loughlin to do the interview without your help.' Katrina narrowed her eyes at him and demanded again, 'Why are you so desperate to keep me from your brother?'

'Because no good will come of it if you find him.' He caught hold of her again. 'Please take the money and go.'

There was something in his eyes that held her to the spot as helplessly as though she had been bound and nailed there. It was a fierceness of emotion whose intensity shook her. It poured through her, immobilising her, numbing her to the core, and yet, at the same time, rubbing her senses raw.

She said in a whisper, 'I'm sorry, I can't.'

Axel said nothing for a moment. He seemed unable to speak. He just continued to look down at her with that fierce, ragged look—part rage, part impatience, part desperation, part pain.

Then, sighing, he closed his eyes and when he opened them again the look of pain and desperation had gone.

'OK,' he said. 'If you insist.'

'I do. I must. I hope you understand.' Suddenly, foolishly, she did hope that. 'I don't want you to think I don't appreciate the gesture... I mean you offering me the money...' She broke off in confusion. What was she doing? Thanking him for offering her a bribe?

But the real reason for her confusion was the way he was holding her, more closely than she had realised, so that she was pressed up against him. She could feel the hardness of his chest through the linen of his jacket thrusting against the softness of her breasts. And the more she became aware of it, the more confused she was growing. And the more excited by the utter sensuality of the feeling.

'If you must, you must.'

His voice was low and gravelly, and Katrina was suddenly aware of his fingers in her hair. A burst of flames shot through her. Her heart was thundering. She knew precisely what was about to happen next.

'I must,' she said, her heart close to exploding.

Then she parted her lips and waited for his kiss.

CHAPTER FOUR

HIS lips brushed hers so gently at first that Katrina wondered if she might be dreaming.

She had closed her eyes as Axel leaned towards her, as though by shutting out the sight of him she could make what was happening less real. For, though she seemed to have lost all power of resistance, she was still filled with a sense of horror at what was happening.

How could she allow this man to kiss her? Why wasn't she fighting him? Why hadn't she moved away? For she could have. Though he was holding her, he was holding her only lightly. He was using no force to keep her where she was.

But all such thoughts and feelings in that bright heady moment somehow seemed like a minor detail. Katrina pushed them aside with no trouble whatsoever and simply sank into the sheer blissful rapture of the moment.

For rapture was what it was, as, drawing her closer, Axel bent to brush his lips against hers. In that moment of contact a bushfire swept through her, setting light to every inch of her, from her scalp to her toes. Suddenly the blood was exploding in her veins.

His fingers were in her hair, exploratory, gentle, whipping her senses into a frenzy. It was as though the touch of him had thrown a switch inside her, turning on sensations she had never known before.

To begin with his kisses were as soft as gossamer, the lightest of brushes, fleeting and tender. Then the arms that circled her tightened their grip a little, and simultaneously the pressure of his lips grew harder.

Katrina could feel a fire in him, an urgency that made her blood jump. Quite involuntarily her hands drifted up to his shoulders, though she knew that was the last thing they ought to be doing. And the more his lips crushed hers, the more she responded. As his tongue flickered against her teeth, her own tongue answered, flickering hungrily to meet his.

Helpless longing pierced through her, sweet and unbearable. And suddenly it was as though all her senses had been laid open, from top to bottom, with a knife.

The hard virile warmth of him pressed against her, the firmness of his chest crushing against her breasts, the taut thighs burning like fire against her own. And the circle of his arms that held her tightly was a prison from which she had no desire to escape. She loved the feel of those strong restraining arms.

Katrina might happily have stayed locked in his arms for ever. Why not? It was the closest thing to heaven she'd ever known. But even as she stood there, breathless with excitement, Axel was starting to move away.

The arms around her slackened. Softly, he drew his head back. As she opened her eyes and looked into his face, he smiled at her. 'Well, well,' he said.

Well, well, indeed. Feeling confused, she smiled back at him. Her heart was still lurching about

inside her. She couldn't think of anything sensible
to say.

'So, have you changed your mind?' Still smiling
that soft smile, Axel reached up to curl a strand of
hair behind her ear.

Katrina looked back at him, stupidly, not understanding. 'Changed my mind about what?' she
wanted to know.

Involuntarily, her eyes drifted over his face, over
the smooth dark brow, the high forceful cheekbones, down to the small pale scar she had noticed
before on his chin. Some foolishness almost
prompted her to reach up and kiss it.

But she pushed that foolishness from her, for
foolishness it was. The whole episode, from start
to finish, had been a massive, shameful foolishness. As she stood there, that was gradually beginning to sink in.

She forced her eyes back to his and drew away
a little as she repeated, 'Have I changed my mind
about what?'

Axel allowed her to move away. His hands
dropped away from her. But as he stood there
before her, only inches away, it felt almost as though
their two bodies were still touching. Their two sep-
arate warmths continued to mingle. They were not
two distinct beings. The space they occupied
was one.

Axel continued to smile at her, eyes like black
velvet. He said, 'About taking the money, *querida*.
I hope you have. It would be the wise thing to do.'

For a moment, quite genuinely, Katrina was
puzzled. She'd entirely forgotten about the money,
about the cheque he had offered and that she had

rejected and that still lay on the floor between them where it had fallen.

But as he repeated his question—'Well, have you, *querida*?'—her puzzlement vanished like mist in bright sunshine. She felt a leap of sudden anger, mingled with fierce disappointment. Had his kisses simply been a ploy to win her round?

'No,' she answered, stepping further away from him. 'I'm afraid I haven't changed my mind.'

And in that instant all sense of oneness vanished. A gulf a mile wide divided them now.

Katrina felt herself shiver. 'I will never change my mind. I've told you already I don't want your money.'

'I'll leave you to think about it.' As she took another step away from him, Axel bent down quickly and picked up the cheque. For a moment he held it pointedly between them. 'It's here,' he said, 'if you should come to your senses. All you have to do is let me know.' Then with a narrow-eyed smile, he folded the cheque again and slipped it into the breast pocket of his jacket.

'Remember this is also your passport to Loughlin,' he added. 'I'll give you twenty-four hours to think about it.'

'I don't need twenty-four hours. I don't need a single minute. I've already told you I'll never take your money. And, besides, I can find my own way to Loughlin.' Katrina faced him angrily, her green eyes sparking. 'I don't need any passport from you!'

Then she turned away, heading for the door, ignoring the cynical smile on his lips and wishing she felt half as confident as she sounded.

*   *   *

Katrina didn't go straight back to her hotel. She worked off some steam first with a brisk walk round the town. Then, thirsty, she stopped for an orange juice at a roadside café.

Damn Axel Jerez! she was thinking. Damn him for making everything so difficult. Though it wasn't just Axel's behaviour that was bothering her. Her own was providing considerable cause for concern.

She took a mouthful of her orange juice and stared down at the tabletop. What had got into her? Why had she allowed Axel to kiss her? And why had she kissed him back like that?

At the memory she shuddered. Though it was an insincere shudder. Even now, just to think of those moments in his arms sent tingles of excitement rushing across her skin.

It was because he'd seemed different, she told herself defensively. He'd seemed tender and warm, not at all the way he usually was. And that had been the cause. She'd been beguiled by the change in him.

Anger filled her. Of course it had all been an act. Really, there'd been nothing different about him at all.

But then she remembered that pained look in his eyes, that look that had been touched with desperation as he'd almost pleaded with her to take the money, leave Tenerife and go back home.

That hadn't been an act, that emotion in his eyes. Whatever he'd been feeling had been fierce and honest. And to a proud man like Axel such pleading would not come easily, yet to protect his brother he'd been prepared to plead. That look in his eyes had been love for his brother.

She felt a dart of sympathy. That was an emotion she understood.

So he wasn't all bad, after all, she acknowledged. He was capable of human feeling, however misguided. But it was more than just this revelation of brotherly love that had catapulted her into the realms of madness. The real cause of that had been something much more personal. She'd allowed herself to believe that he felt some warmth for her.

It was his offer of the money that had made her think it. For it had seemed for a moment that he was offering it out of kindness. He'd said, 'You deserve to have your money back. I don't want you to be out of pocket.' And the words had been accompanied by a look of such sincerity that she had actually believed he really meant them.

Now she dismissed that as ridiculous and scorned her own gullibility. He's smart, she told herself. He's smart and he's cynical. He's capable of making anyone believe anything he wants. And he certainly did a good job of fooling me. He caught me off guard and I fell for it like a mug.

She frowned into her orange juice. But from now on she'd be smart too.

It was at that precise moment that something made her glance up. A car horn, perhaps, or some uncanny sixth sense. And her heart leapt as she recognised, parked across the street, Axel's gleaming black Mercedes.

He was seated at the wheel and, as Katrina looked at him, she couldn't quite smother a quick dart of pleasure. In that instant the sun seemed to shine a little more brightly.

But then she froze, her pleasure dying. Axel was not alone.

Seated at his side was a beautiful young woman, dark-haired and wearing a bright yellow dress. And from the look of things, as Katrina peered across at them, the two of them were involved in a heated quarrel.

At least, the woman was involved, her face distorted as she shouted at him. Axel sat silently, eyes fixed straight ahead, a look of dark impatience on his face.

And then, suddenly, the woman was climbing from the car and angrily slamming the door shut behind her. Then she was turning on her heel and storming off down the street, her sleek dark hair swinging as she walked.

Wide-eyed, motionless, Katrina continued to stare as, without even a backward glance at the departing woman, Axel steered the car back into the traffic and headed off in the opposite direction.

Who was the woman? Katrina sat rigidly in her seat and watched as the black Mercedes disappeared. She felt cold from head to toe. Perhaps the woman was no one special. Just some casual acquaintance with whom he'd clearly fallen out.

She stared down at her orange juice, iron bars in her stomach, shocked at how desperately she wanted to believe that. But she knew it wasn't so. That woman was no casual acquaintance. Katrina had sensed an intimacy between them. That woman was either his girlfriend or his wife.

His wife.

A sick sensation rushed through. Was Axel married, after all?

She fought to control the sick feeling. It doesn't matter, she told herself. Why should I care? He's nothing to me.

But as she reached for her orange juice, her hand was shaking so violently that she almost spilled her drink in her lap. And though she tried to sweep it from her she couldn't quite conquer the sense of bleak misery that had curled around her heart.

'So you're still here? I thought you said you were leaving?'

Katrina had been sitting on her bed watching TV when suddenly the phone at her bedside had rung. She flinched a little now, recognising Axel's voice, though he hadn't actually had the grace to introduce himself.

But she'd had time to gather herself since her shock this afternoon when she'd seen him quarrelling with his wife—for that was who it was, she'd become more and more certain—and now she composed herself very quickly.

She told him, 'Yes, I'm still here. Sorry if you're disappointed.' She paused. 'Was there anything in particular you wanted?'

He did not answer her question. 'I'm at your hotel,' he informed her. Then with the hint of a smile in his voice, he demanded, 'Are you dressed? How quickly can you meet me down in the lobby?'

Katrina frowned into the phone. The nerve of the man! 'I could probably be down in less than ten minutes.' She paused, then took pleasure in adding carefully, 'That is if I had any intention of coming down, of course.'

'Oh, I think you'll come down.'

'What makes you think that?'

'Because if you don't, I'm afraid I'll have to come up. And I suspect you would prefer our meeting to take place in a public place rather than in the intimacy of your bedroom.'

Katrina felt herself flush at that and was glad he couldn't see her. For he couldn't have been more right. After what had passed between them this morning—and even more so now that she was almost certain he was married—she would not feel at all happy about receiving him in her bedroom!

But all the same she told him, 'I'm not coming down, and you won't be setting foot inside my room, either. You see, I've no intention of allowing you through the door.'

Axel laughed at that, that rich open laugh that every time she heard it made her want to laugh with him. He said, 'What are you doing that's so important, anyway? Perhaps you're already entertaining some gentleman friend?'

'Perhaps I am, and perhaps I don't wish to be interrupted.' There was a smile in her voice as she responded to his teasing. Perhaps a little too much of a smile, she decided, instantly sobering her tone and adding, 'Actually what I was doing was watching TV. I've had a very busy day and I was planning an early night.'

'Not this early, surely? It's only just after ten.' Then, before she could respond, he added quickly, 'So, put on some clothes and be down in the lobby in ten minutes.' He paused for just a second. 'If you're not, I'll be up.' And then, to Katrina's dismay, the phone went dead.

She stared at it in angry silence for a moment. How dared he presume to commandeer her like this? Demanding to see her without even giving a reason!

On that thought her eyes narrowed. But maybe there was a reason and perhaps it would be in her interests to do as he said. Besides, she had no desire to suffer the irritation of him making a public scene outside her bedroom door—something of which she suspected he was perfectly capable.

If he was determined to see her, then he would see her. It was simply the way Axel Jerez was made.

Just over ten minutes later, dressed in a peacock-blue dress with a wide scooped neckline and cinched-in waist, Katrina stepped out of the lift into the hotel lobby. She saw Axel instantly, standing by the reception desk, and to her deepest consternation her heart lit up like a light bulb. She had to smother the foolish smile that rose to her lips.

He was dressed in an elegant light grey suit, with a plain white shirt and a red-patterned tie. And there was no doubt about it, Katrina thought sadly, he was quite simply the most stunning-looking man she'd ever seen.

Next moment he had caught sight of her and was heading towards her across the lobby.

'So, you just made it.' The black eyes were smiling, teasing her as he stood there looking down at her. 'Another few seconds and I would have been on my way upstairs.'

It was tempting to joke back at him, but Katrina resisted the temptation. Joking might be misconstrued as flirting. And flirting was definitely out of bounds.

She averted her eyes and told him in a brisk voice, 'Yes, I'm here. So perhaps you wouldn't mind telling me why you wanted to see me so urgently?'

'I'm curious to hear about the busy day you've had.' He smiled a teasing smile. 'Let's go out into the garden and you can tell me all about it.'

Then he paused, one eyebrow lifting. 'I'm presuming you've eaten. If you haven't, we can go to the restaurant and order you some dinner.' He smiled. 'Though I'm afraid I won't be able to join you. I've just had dinner with a business associate. Our meeting finished early, so I thought I'd give you a ring.'

'You had dinner here?' Katrina glanced up at him.

He nodded. 'I often entertain my business associates here.'

'I see.' She glanced away, feeling a warm tingle inside her to realise that while she'd been sitting up in her room Axel had been here in the very same building. But she squashed it instantly. She had no right to feel such things.

She said, 'Yes, I've had dinner. I ate in my room.'

'In that case, let's go and have a stroll in the garden.'

As he spoke, he touched her elbow, very lightly. But the sheen electric impact of that fleeting contact sent Katrina instantly shooting forward. Before he could touch her again, she was through the door like a rocket. Just the merest touch of him made her unravel inside.

It was a blissfully balmy evening, the sky full of stars, the still, silent gardens drenched in moonlight. A narrow paved path meandered between the palm trees, skirting the deserted swimming-pool and the open-air restaurant, heading down in shady darkness towards the beach edge.

'So, what's been keeping you so busy?' Axel was walking alongside her. 'I thought what you'd be doing was booking your flight home.'

'Then I'm afraid you were wrong.' Katrina was keeping a careful distance, terrified that his arm might brush against hers. 'On the contrary, I've been getting on with what I came for—trying to pin down Fergus Loughlin.'

'With any success?' His tone was amused, as though he already knew the answer.

'Unfortunately, no. He refused to take my calls. But I delivered a letter by hand to his housekeeper setting out a whole list of very persuasive reasons as to why he should take part in the programme——'

She broke off as at that moment a couple appeared round a corner, arm in arm, walking towards them. Axel extended one hand to guide Katrina in front of him, in order to make space for the couple to pass. But, avoiding his hand, Katrina slipped back behind him, keeping a safe half-dozen paces between them. Her heart had leapt at the thought of that hand on her flesh again.

Once the couple had passed, she stepped alongside him once more, irritated by the way her heart was still racing. 'As I was saying, I've delivered a letter arguing my case. I'll give him till tomorrow evening to get in touch with me, then if he doesn't I'll go round to his villa again.'

'Persistent, aren't you? A regular little mosquito.'

'I'm just trying to do my job.' Katrina threw him a sharp look. 'In spite of the obstacles that have been placed in my path.'

'But you're wasting your time. Loughlin doesn't want to play ball with you.' Axel met her gaze with a look of amused indifference. 'You told me yourself that's what he said in his note.'

He spoke with such innocence, as though he were a mere observer, instead of the architect of all her problems. Katrina felt her anger rise. She turned to face him.

'How did you do it? Did you threaten him or something?' A sudden thought occurred to her. 'Or perhaps you simply offered him money? After all, that seems to be a favourite ploy of yours—offering people money to do what you want.'

'Unfortunately, it doesn't always work.' Quite unruffled, Axel glanced down at her. 'Though perhaps in your case I simply didn't offer enough. Yes, perhaps that's it.' He surveyed her critically. 'Perhaps to get rid of you I simply need to up my offer.'

At that moment another couple appeared round another corner. But this time, before Axel could even reach out his hand, Katrina had stepped behind him to let the couple past. And as she and Axel walked in single file for a moment she glared with sharp hostility at his back.

That remark of his had hurt her, deeply and unexpectedly. How dared he suggest that she could be bought? The instant the couple had passed them she shot out from behind him and told him in an angry tone,

'Why don't you put me to the test? Go on, offer me more money! Then just wait and see what I tell you to do with it!'

Axel merely smiled at her little outburst. Then he glanced down at her disparagingly. 'Don't be so hasty, *señorita*. You don't yet know how much I might be prepared to offer.'

'It wouldn't make any difference.'

'As I said, don't be so hasty. I'm sure if I decided to be generous, we could very easily come to an arrangement.'

'Never!'

Hurt and anger went pouring through her. She'd been wrong to believe he cared anything about anything—and certainly that he cared about her losing the money. All he cared about was cynically protecting his brother. And it didn't matter to him if he offended and insulted her in the process.

Smothering her hurt, she shot him a look of contempt. 'You know, people like you really disgust me!'

'Disgust?' Through an overhead gap in the palm trees a sudden shaft of moonlight fell across him, illuminating the dark hair, touching it with silver, sharpening the hard bony planes of his face. He regarded her cynically. 'I've detected many emotions in you on the various occasions we've been together, but I can't say that one of them has ever been disgust.'

As he finished the sentence, he turned to meet her eyes, and she knew that he was thinking of their encounter this morning. Certainly there'd been no hint of disgust in her response then! Quite the contrary. All there'd been was pure helpless attraction!

And, even now, making her feel vulnerable, that attraction remained. The disgust she'd talked about was all in her head.

She glanced away, feeling exposed and awkward, and for a minute or two they walked together in silence. Then she turned to look at him. 'Why did you want to see me? Was it in order to offer me more money?'

As she had half expected, he did not answer her. He had an irritating habit of not answering her questions. Instead, he said, 'So, what have you been doing, apart from making fruitless efforts to change Loughlin's mind?'

'Don't be so hasty.' Katrina smiled a dry smile as she deliberately tossed his own words back at him. 'You don't know yet whether they've been fruitless or not. Personally, I expect them to be anything but.'

'I admire your optimism.'

'Not optimism. Determination.'

'Well, whatever you want to call it, I admire it.'

As he spoke, he held her gaze with eyes as black as velvet, smiling, sending a shaft of swift excitement through her, a sensation as a sharp as steel and as sweet as honey. With a silent gasp Katrina dropped her gaze.

She stared at the ground, willing the sensation to leave her. 'You asked me what else I've been doing,' she put to him, reaching for a subject that would put some distance between them. 'Well, one thing I've been doing is collecting some more names of people who can help me track down Jaime.'

For she'd made a call to Irene just after lunch, urging her to dig up a few more contacts. Irene, to

Katrina's relief, had sounded a lot better, and after a moment's thought she had duly obliged.

Axel seemed unconcerned. 'I wish you luck,' he told her, though it was perfectly plain he wished her no such thing.

And it was irritating how he seemed so sure she would fail. Another thought struck Katrina. 'How have you done it?' she demanded. 'It's you who's at the back of your brother's friends' silence, isn't it? I thought they were just keeping quiet out of loyalty to Jaime, knowing that he didn't want to be found. But that was stupid of me, wasn't it? Their silence isn't out of loyalty. It's because you've bought them, just as you buy everyone.'

'Everyone except you, it seems.'

To her annoyance, he was smiling. How could he smile in the face of an accusation like that? Katrina turned on him angrily. 'You're totally unscrupulous. The most unscrupulous man I've ever met!'

'Unscrupulous and disgusting. Don't forget disgusting.' Axel simply smiled a little more widely.

To her dismay Katrina flushed. He'd called her bluff on that already! Then she clenched her fists. 'Yes,' she retorted, 'you're totally unscrupulous, you don't care about anything—and you're perfectly right, that does disgust me!'

There was a shimmering silence as she ended her tirade. Her heart was pounding like a cannon. She looked into his face with a sense of miserable impotence. If only she really meant these things she was saying. Or if only there was no need to mean them at all.

Then she caught her breath as suddenly he reached out to her. He smiled a soft smile. 'Come here,' he said.

Katrina felt her heart stand still. And just for a moment she felt almost overpowered by a sudden thrust of longing to do exactly as he said.

But she would not obey him. Angrily, she snatched her arm away. 'Leave me alone,' she snapped.

But he had caught her arm too quickly and was drawing her towards him, making her heart fly to her throat and her limbs turn to water.

'Come here,' he said again, still smiling that soft smile. Then he added, 'I think these people want to get past.'

'What people?'

It was only then, as she followed his gaze, that Katrina finally noticed the other couple, whose path she'd been blocking.

She turned to apologise. 'I'm terribly sorry.' She felt foolish and relieved and disappointed all at once. She'd thought that 'come here' had meant something else.

But, as the couple moved past them, Axel continued to hold her. And though Katrina was unsure how it had happened, the fact was that she was now leaning lightly against him. His heat was sending rods of lightning through her.

'That's better.' Through blurred eyes she saw him smiling down at her. 'Relax,' he told her. 'I like you better when you're relaxed.'

Katrina felt as though she was trying to strain away from him, but she must have imagined it, for in fact she didn't move a muscle. She remained standing where she was, her whole body burning, finding it increasingly difficult to breathe.

Axel smiled down at her. 'You've been acting all rigid and formal. Keeping your distance, as though you were afraid I might eat you.' His chin brushed her hair. 'I like it much better when you're like this.'

To her dismay Katrina was finding she liked it much better, too. She liked the strange familiarity of his arms about her and the way the warm touch of him seemed to melt her very bones. With every shred of her being she longed to succumb.

She looked up into his face, her eyes grazing his lips, longing to feel those lips against hers. And why not? she found herself thinking, her will-power sagging. What possible harm could there be in a kiss?

But then, as he leaned towards her, a vision sprang before her of that scene she'd witnessed from the café this morning. He wasn't free! How could she have forgotten?

With a gasp she sprang away from him. 'No!' she exclaimed. 'Get away from me! You're not going to trick me like that again.'

'Trick you? Who's tricking you? I wasn't aware of employing trickery. It seemed to me my intentions were perfectly plain.'

His eyes sparkled in the moonlight, full of magic and seduction, and it took all of Katrina's will-power to take another step away.

She was trembling, her mouth dry as she forced herself to speak, surprised at how coherent she managed to sound. 'In that case, allow me to make *my* intentions plain, too. If you've finished with

me, I intend to go back to my room and have that
early night I promised myself.'

He had released her but stood unmoving,
watching her as she faced him. 'I wouldn't exactly
say I'd finished with you,' he said softly. 'On the
contrary,' he added, smiling, 'I hadn't even started.
But if an early night's what you want...' He
shrugged. 'Don't let me stop you.'

'No, I won't. I've no intention of letting you stop
me.' Katrina was backing away from him, appalled
that her limbs were shaking. How was it possible
that he could have this effect on her when he hadn't
even kissed her?

She made to turn on her heel. 'Goodnight,' she
said.

'Wait!'

But she ignored him and kept on going.

'Wait, Katrina. There's something I have to say.'

There was something in his tone that made her
falter. She half turned to look at him. 'Yes?' she
said.

He was standing beneath the palm trees, his
hands in his pockets, a shaft of moonlight in his
hair. And, as she looked at him, Katrina's heart
was weeping. If he says, 'Come,' I shall go to him,
she thought with a sob of pain.

'*Querida*, tell me something...'

He was standing very still. So still he seemed
hardly to be breathing. Even the glint of the jet-
black eyes was lost in shadow. Katrina waited,
watching him. In that moment all she longed for
was for him to invite her to step back into his arms.

She swallowed hard. 'What do you want
to know?'

'What I want to know is this...' He paused for a moment. Then in a flat voice he put to her, 'Since six isn't enough, is ten any better? Will you leave if I give you ten thousand pounds?'

It was as though he had hit her. Katrina felt herself reel inwardly. She shook her head helplessly, unable to speak.

Then she was turning on her heel and running back up the path, a shocked, fleeing figure in the shadow of the palm trees, praying she might never set eyes on him again.

Katrina slept badly that night and woke late, feeling edgy. Don't think of Axel Jerez, she told herself firmly. Just try to put him out of your mind. To think of Axel made her stomach churn with anger.

The first thing she did—before she'd even had breakfast—was make a phone call to Fergus Loughlin's villa.

'Did you give him my letter?' she asked the housekeeper who answered. 'What did he say? Is there any reply?'

'No reply.' The housekeeper didn't waste words with her. 'Goodbye,' she added briskly, then hung up the phone.

Katrina thought for a moment. She'd already decided yesterday to give Loughlin till tonight before going back to his villa, but in the meantime she didn't plan to waste the rest of the day. She'd hire a car and drive around the island hunting for suitable locations for interviews. After all, in the end she was going to need them!

As it turned out, she discovered a few that looked perfect. Katrina returned to her hotel that evening in high spirits. Now, before she did anything else, she'd give Loughlin another ring.

But she never made that phone call, for as she was picking up her room key the desk clerk handed her an envelope, telling her, 'This was handed in earlier for you.'

Katrina stood in the lift and stared at the plain white envelope, on which, in a firm hand, her name was written in blue ink. And somehow she knew beyond a shadow of doubt that that stylish confident hand was Axel's.

She thought with a sense of sickness, He's sent me the cheque. He really does think that he can buy me.

Her fingers trembled. Should she tear the envelope into pieces or simply send it back to him unopened?

But she did neither. Illogically, she needed the proof that he really was capable of such a despicable act. It would make it that much easier never to think of him again.

She stepped out of the lift and headed for her room, tearing the envelope open with impatient fingers. Then, once inside her room, she drew out the contents.

It was not a cheque. She could see that instantly. What it was was something far more surprising.

CHAPTER FIVE

'WELL, now! If it isn't my favourite redhead!'

As Katrina stepped into the huge hall with a smile at the housekeeper who had come to open the big front door for her, Axel appeared from the drawing-room, looking quite spectacular in a cream-coloured suit and matching shirt.

He smiled as he came towards her. 'So, you decided to come. I suspected you'd be unable to resist the bait.'

'I hope it wasn't a hoax.'

Katrina looked into his face, feeling a helpless thrust of emotion go through her. It was ridiculous, but seeing him had suddenly made her realise that she couldn't have borne it if she'd never seen him again. I must be out of my mind, she told herself sharply.

'A hoax?' He was smiling down at her, dark eyes twinkling. 'Do I strike you as the sort of man who would invite a young lady to join him and some friends at his home for dinner as a hoax?'

She could have answered that in one single affirmative syllable! But instead, she smiled an oblique smile. 'Of course not,' she told him. 'And I'm sure what you implied in your letter was genuine ... and Fergus Loughlin really is here.' She paused. 'When you said someone I was keen to meet would be here, I take it you meant Fergus Loughlin and not Jaime?'

'Which would you prefer?'

'Ideally, I'd like both of them. But if I have to choose, for the moment I'd choose Loughlin.'

'Then you're in luck, *querida*.'

'Does that mean he's here?'

Axel shrugged. 'Not yet. But he will be shortly.'

'You're quite sure of that?'

Katrina looked into his face, her optimism touched by suspicion and hurt as she forced herself to remember what he was capable of. Perhaps he had simply lured her here to torment her—or to offer her more money to leave Tenerife.

'If you're not sure,' she added, 'I'd rather just leave now.'

Axel smiled a slow smile, as though he had read her mind. 'My, what a suspicious nature,' he observed. 'Are you always, *querida*, as untrusting as this?'

'No.' She regarded him squarely. 'And I don't have a suspicious nature. But I've grown used to you standing in my way all the time. This sudden change of tactics comes as rather a shock.'

Axel simply smiled more broadly. 'I'm sorry if I shocked you. I can assure you that was not my intention.' He paused and let his eyes drift over her unhurriedly. 'However, I must say your state of shock greatly becomes you.'

A silly blush touched Katrina's cheeks as with open appreciation his gaze drifted over her tall, slender figure in the scoop-necked violet dress she was wearing. She felt suddenly aware of how the dress exposed her neck and shoulders and afforded just a glimpse of sun-kissed cleavage.

She'd worn it because it was the only dress she had with her that was suitable for what she'd suspected would be a fairly dressy occasion. And besides it was one of her favourites and she knew its soft lines flattered her. But now, ridiculously, it made her feel quite provocative.

'I'm glad you left your hair loose.' To further add to her confusion, Axel reached out suddenly and brushed fleetingly with his fingers one gleaming strand of bright red hair. 'So many women with long hair like to put it up when they go to dinner parties. I would have been most disappointed if you'd made that mistake.'

'I sometimes put it up.' Though he was no longer touching her, his gaze still lingered over her halo of rich red curls. I wish I'd put it up tonight, she was thinking. In fact, I might just slip into the nearest bathroom and screw it into the tightest little bun I can manage!

He seemed to read her thoughts. 'Always leave it as it is. To hide that hair would be like keeping a Rembrandt in a cupboard. Hair like that was made to be seen and admired.'

Then, with a smile, he turned away. 'Come and meet the other guests.'

Katrina followed as he led her through to the drawing-room where a dozen or so people were gathered in small groups, chatting and laughing and drinking champagne. And suddenly she was aware of a gathering apprehension. All at once there was a knot in the pit of her stomach. This is where I meet her, she was thinking sickly. His wife or his girlfriend or whatever she is. Her eyes scanned the little groups for the dark-haired woman.

But there was no sign of the woman she had seen quarrelling with him the other morning. Perhaps she was in the kitchen overseeing the dinner.

Axel led her towards one of the groups. 'This is Katrina MacGregor,' he was saying, as half a dozen faces turned towards her. 'She's in television in Britain.'

'Oh, how fascinating. Are you based in London?' As Axel finished the introductions, Sofía, a striking-looking woman in black, turned to Katrina with a questioning smile.

Katrina shook her head. 'No. Edinburgh,' she answered. 'I work for a local company there.'

'Ah, Scotland! How wonderful! I just adore Scotland!' Sofía's husband, Antonio, joined in the conversation. 'All those ancient castles and all that fabulous scenery. My wife and I once had a wonderful holiday there.'

'Do you live in a castle?' Axel joined in now, teasing. 'I can just imagine you up on the ramparts, red hair flying in the misty Scottish breeze.'

'No, I don't live in a castle.' Katrina grimaced politely back at him. 'As I told you, I live in the centre of Edinburgh.'

'But there's a castle in the centre of Edinburgh.' The other guests smiled as he continued to tease her, dark eyes flashing with amusement. 'And a very ancient and distinguished castle it is. If you ask me, in the splendid castle is where you belong.'

So do you—in its deepest, darkest dungeon! What did he think he was up to flirting with her like this when his other half was probably in the next room?

Katrina narrowed her eyes at him, hiding her discomfort from the other guests. 'Well, I'm afraid I live in a very modest flat. TV researchers can't afford to live in castles.'

She was glad she'd said that. It took her mind off her discomfort and instantly reminded her of her reason for being here. Work. Her research. Fergus Loughlin. She took a deep breath and glanced over Axel's shoulder, her eyes focusing expectantly on the open doorway, hoping to see the missing sculptor walk through it.

But, instead, her breath caught as in that very instant a dark-haired woman came walking through it instead. Katrina very nearly dropped her glass of champagne.

But then the woman turned towards her, just as Sofía was saying, 'Katrina, tell us about the kind of work you do?' and, as Katrina looked into the woman's face, her frozen heart began to beat again. It was not the woman she had seen with Axel in the car.

She turned back to Sofía. 'My work?' she answered, smiling, making a good job of hiding the way her heart was still racing. 'What can I tell you about it? It's the best job in the world.'

Get a grip on yourself, she was silently telling herself. Sooner or later, you're going to meet her, and it would be preferable if you could handle it with a bit of poise!

The meeting seemed destined to take place later rather than sooner, however, and twenty minutes later Katrina had forgotten all about this uncomfortable little threat that was hanging over her.

She'd become totally involved in the conversation and was actually having a thoroughly good time.

I rather like Axel's friends, she found herself thinking, less surprised than she would once have been at this revelation. Once, she could not have imagined liking anything about him. It would appear her attitude towards him had changed.

Though perhaps she was being rash, she told herself crisply. Perhaps she had no cause to alter her attitude—for there was still no sign of the missing sculptor!

Indeed there was still no sign of him as they all sat down to dinner—round a huge oval table set with sparkling crystal and gleaming silver, with a glorious arrangement of flowers in the centre—and waited while the first course of seafood salad was served.

And not only was there no sign of Fergus Loughlin. There was no sign of the mysterious dark-haired woman either. Axel had seated himself at the head of the table, but the place opposite him at the other end remained unoccupied.

How very odd, Katrina was thinking, trying very hard not to feel too hopeful. But in spite of her efforts, her hopes were spiralling. Maybe the dark-haired woman wasn't his wife, after all. Maybe she wasn't even a girlfriend. Maybe she was just what Katrina had hoped in the beginning—nothing but a casual acquaintance.

She slipped a look along the table to where Axel was seated, feeling her heart suddenly skip and dance inside her. Maybe she'd been going through all this suffering for nothing. Maybe Axel was free. Maybe he had no other half!

'I hope you're hungry.'

Katrina spun round almost guiltily, as Sofía, who was sitting opposite her, suddenly spoke. She felt the excitement in her heart must be spilling from her eyes. It was suddenly so intense she thought she might explode.

I know I'm right, she was thinking, but I have to find out for sure!

Sofía continued, unaware of Katrina's inner turmoil, 'The Jerez dinner parties tend to be like banquets. Never fewer than a dozen courses.'

Katrina answered automatically. 'A dozen courses? My goodness!'

She glanced again at Axel, almost bursting. I have to find out! I have to find out!

Sofía was nodding. 'At least a dozen,' she confirmed. 'Axel is nothing if not a generous host.'

'Oh, I'm sure he is.' Katrina laughed foolishly, darting another quick glance at Axel, who seemed engrossed in chatting to a grey-haired woman.

How gorgeous he was. How gorgeous and how generous. And free! She bit her lip. But she had to find out for sure!

Her heart squeezed within her. She turned back to Sofía. And here, right before her, was the very person who could tell her!

Controlling her expression carefully, though her eyes were still sparkling, Katrina smiled at Sofía and observed almost flippantly, 'I must say I was just wondering why there's no hostess. But I suppose that's because——'

But she got no further.

'Oh, that. Oh, dear.' Sofía's expression had grown mournful. She lowered her voice to a whisper and leaned across the table. 'A tragedy, of course. Who would have expected it? But I'm told we won't be seeing her any more.' She shook her head with a sigh. 'Such a sad situation.'

Katrina had frozen in her seat, her sparkle extinguished. She felt as though Sofía had thrown cold water in her face. And she could already feel her stomach shrink within her and knew that she didn't want to hear any more as Sofía added, demolishing any hope that remained,

'The break-up of a marriage is such a sad thing. And I hear there's even been talk of divorce.'

Katrina had gone quite numb, her cheeks the colour of the ivory tablecloth. Suddenly everything seemed to be crashing about her. Axel was married, after all. The dark-haired woman was his wife.

She stared down at her plate, struggling to pull herself together, only a little reassured that through her sense of acute anguish one corner of her heart felt sympathy for Axel. As Sofía had said, a marriage break-up was a sad thing.

But what was far, far sadder to her at that moment was the fact that there was a marriage to break up in the first place. One day Axel might be free, but he was not free now. No matter which way you looked at it, he was married.

She cast him a quick look, steeling her heart as she did so. At least she should be grateful that at last she knew the truth.

Then she picked up her fork and observed to Sofía, who thankfully, had already changed the subject, 'This seafood salad looks absolutely delicious!'

It turned out to be even more delicious than it looked, but Katrina had only taken a couple of mouthfuls when, suddenly the dining-room door burst open, and through it came barging, red-faced with apology, the portly, bearded figure of Fergus Loughlin.

'So sorry I'm late, Axel.' He made an apologetic gesture towards his host. 'But you know me...miles away as usual... I was working and had no idea it was so late.'

'No harm done. It's good to see you.' Axel, smiling, had risen politely in his seat. He gestured towards the empty chair next to Sofía. 'You haven't missed anything. We've only just started.'

Then, as Loughlin bustled to his place, Axel glanced at Katrina and treated her to an amused and very pointed wink. There, he seemed to be saying, 'o thou of little faith'!

Katrina dropped her gaze away, confused for a moment by a sudden fierce surge of extremely mixed feelings. She was delighted to see Loughlin, of course, but, perversely, at the same time she was rather sorry that Axel hadn't let her down, after all. It would, she reflected wryly, have made things easier.

Then Axel proceeded to make things even more difficult by saying to Loughlin, 'That young lady opposite you, the rather stunning redhead, is the one I was telling you about from the TV station. As I think you already know, she's very anxious to meet you.'

Katrina took a deep breath. The perversity of fate! The minute I discover he's not free he starts being charming!

Then, taking the initiative, she leaned across the table towards the sculptor. 'I'm a great admirer of your work, Mr Loughlin. I do hope you'll change your mind about doing the interview...'

Loughlin glanced across at her. 'Thank you,' he told her. Then with an awkward little shrug, he added, 'We'll see...' And, with that, he proceeded to attack his seafood salad.

Sofía hadn't been exaggerating about the dinner. It turned out there were fourteen courses in all, each one more delicious than the one before. And it was quite simply the best meal Katrina had ever tasted.

When it was over, she and some of the other guests drifted out to the terrace where brandy and liqueurs and coffee were being served. Alone for a moment, she leaned against the railings and gazed out seawards to where a huge pale moon hung in a dark blue velvet sky. Paradise, she found herself thinking again.

'Well, did you catch your fish?'

Suddenly Axel was at her elbow. The devil, Katrina thought, as she half turned to face at him. But it was a wistful, affectionate thought, without any malice. It seemed a long time since she had last thought of him as *el diablo*.

She smiled at him. 'Fergus Loughlin, you mean? No, I haven't quite landed him yet. He's still refusing to commit himself.'

Axel was carrying two glasses. He handed her one. 'Drambuie,' he told her. 'I hope you like it. I decided I couldn't go wrong with one of your national drinks.'

Katrina accepted it with a pleased nod. 'Thanks. It's my favourite.' Then she took a sip as Axel continued,

'Fergus'll come round in the end. I'm sure of it. It's just that, like all creative people, he can be a bit eccentric at times.'

'I think you're right. I think he will come round.' Katrina turned more fully to face him as she spoke, and there was a look of apology in her green eyes. For now, having met Loughlin, she realised she'd been wrong about something. 'I'm sorry I accused you of being behind his change of mind. I realise now you had nothing to do with it.'

'That's all right. I'm used to being blamed for things I didn't do.'

As Axel smiled a wry smile and leaned against the railings, ever so fleetingly his sleeve brushed Katrina's arm. It felt like the faintest of caresses. Delicious and forbidden.

He added, watching her, 'If you'd known Fergus Loughlin, you'd have known he's not a man to do another's bidding.' He smiled. 'Particularly not for money. In that respect, *querida*, he's really rather a lot like you.'

Katrina fought back a blush. That had sounded like praise. The warmth in his voice had caught her unawares.

She looked back at him. 'Yes, that was the impression I got, too—that Fergus is very much his own man. I could see at once that I'd been wrong to blame you.'

However, there remained one mystery. She narrowed her eyes curiously. 'Why did you invite me here to meet him, knowing I would probably succeed in winning him round? Even though it wasn't you who changed his mind in the first place, I thought that rather suited your strategy—to make me give up on the interview and quit Tenerife and forget about trying to track down your brother...?'

'Perhaps I've changed my strategy.' Axel sipped his brandy and smiled at her. 'Clearly, I underestimated your professionalism at the beginning. I can see now you're not about to leave the island until you've done the job you came for...'

He shrugged. 'Perhaps I decided to give you a hand in that direction—and then just hope you'd leave as soon as you'd done.'

'Just hope? That sounds a little passive for you!' Katrina laughed in a display of astonished amusement. 'You mean you haven't got any plans to eject me forcibly?'

'As a matter of fact I haven't.'

'Now, that surprises me.' She laughed again. 'Well, I could be here for some time. After all, Loughlin hasn't agreed to anything yet. Winning him round could take a while.'

'I doubt it.' Axel watched her over the rim of his brandy glass. 'How could he resist you now that he's met you? How could any red-blooded man resist a girl like you?'

'You have.'

She said it too quickly, to camouflage her sudden embarrassment. The way he was looking at her was making the blood rush and her skin was prickling as though touched by hot needles. She'd felt a sudden urgent need to push him away.

But it had been the wrong thing to say. That was perfectly obvious as he responded with one of those

light, teasing smiles of his, that at times could
border on the openly flirtatious, and responded,
'Have I resisted you? I hadn't noticed.'

'What I meant was that you've resisted my pleas
regarding Jaime.' Instantly, she rushed to put him
right. 'And you've resisted, apparently, without any
trouble at all.'

But, once again, she'd left the way open for mis-
interpretation. His eyes sparkled at her. 'Who said
it was without any trouble at all? No, *querida*, resisting you has not been easy.'

'Nevertheless, you have.' Katrina held her glass
tightly. Her heart was bouncing like a rubber ball
inside her. 'You may flatter me all you like, but
you've still refused to help me.'

'And I shall continue to refuse to help you—
though it will continue not to be easy.' The smile
never left his eyes. His mouth crinkled at the
corners. 'Though with any other favour you care
to ask of me I'm sure you can count on me to
oblige.'

'There is no other favour I want to ask you.' Her
gaze drifted awkwardly away from his eyes, down
to his mouth and to the small scar on his chin. Then
curiously she glanced up again. 'How did you get
that scar?'

It seemed an oddly intimate question, but
somehow far less intimate than what was passing
between them at that moment. As his expression
altered slightly, one eyebrow lifting, she felt a sense
of deep relief, like escaping from quicksand.

'This scar?' He raised his free hand to touch his
chin with his finger. His fingernail gleamed pale

against the darkness of his skin, and he really did have the most perfectly shaped hands.

'Yes,' Katrina answered, feeling the quicksand round her feet again and hastily shifting her gaze back to his eyes.

'A childhood accident.' He took a mouthful of his drink. 'Jaime was fooling around with my bicycle one day. When he fell I tried to save him and ended up with this.'

'Rushing to protect your brother again? It seems to be a lifelong habit.'

'You disapprove?'

'Not about the incident with the bicycle. No, of course I don't disapprove of that. Besides,' she added recklessly, 'the scar rather suits you.' Then, horrified that she could possibly have said such a thing, she hurried on, 'It's your current protective stance I disapprove of. But then, of course, you already know that.'

'Yes, I already know that.'

The dark eyes seemed to swallow her as he stood there in silence looking down at her. And suddenly Katrina didn't know where to look. She dared not look at his eyes and every time she looked away from them her gaze seemed to drift down to that oddly alluring scar. She found herself staring fixedly at his tie.

'But surely you're as guilty as I am? Possibly even guiltier.'

'Guiltier?' Katrina swallowed drily. The colours of his tie were all swimming together out of focus. 'Guiltier of what?' she demanded huskily, for all at once she did feel quite alarmingly guilty.

'Guilty,' he answered, 'of over-protectiveness towards a sibling.'

'Oh, that . . .' She took a quick mouthful of Drambuie. 'I'm not protecting Irene,' she told him. 'All I'm doing is doing her a favour. She's hit a bad patch. She needs my help.'

There was a pause as Axel drained his brandy glass and laid it down on a nearby table. Then he said, 'If you got it, would you really give that money back to Irene? If I were in your shoes, I'm afraid I'd just keep it.'

'No doubt you would.' She remembered what Irene had told her, about how he had refused his brother all financial help. 'But then you would never have lent it to her in the first place.'

'No, I wouldn't.'

He leaned more comfortably against the railings, again brushing her arm lightly with the sleeve of his jacket. And to her shame Katrina wished his arms had lingered a little longer. She longed to feel the hard warmth of him press against her.

She drained her Drambuie, praying it might dilute the feeling. 'Irene needs the money,' she said.

'What for? You said she's not interested in going into business any more.'

'No, she's not. But she wants to do a course. A beautician's course. Down in London.'

Axel gave a shout of laughter, just as she'd known he would. She caught a glimpse of even, perfectly white teeth. And, as always, his laugh made her want to laugh with him. She struggled not to and demanded, 'What's funny about that?'

'Everything. That sister of yours will never finish her beautician's course—even if she ever starts it, which I very much doubt.'

'She *will* finish it. She's always wanted to be a beautician.'

He was still smiling. 'I thought she always wanted to go into business?'

'I never said that. I think that idea came from Jaime—probably just so he could put his hands on that money.' She frowned. 'No, Irene's serious about this beautician's course. She's been talking on and off about doing it for years.'

'More off than on, I've no doubt.' Axel shook his head. 'Why won't you just accept the fact that your sister's a waster?'

'Because she's not. Don't say that. All she needs is a chance.'

'And you very generously plan to finance that chance.' He shook his head again, his eyes flowing over her. 'Perhaps, if you knew the truth about her, you wouldn't be so keen.'

'What truth?' Katrina looked back at him, suddenly remembering something he had said to her the other day at the deserted flat. She narrowed her green eyes at him. 'Nothing you could ever tell me could alter my feelings for Irene or my determination to help her...' She paused. 'But what exactly did you mean when you said that Irene had lied to me and that it would be so easy to prove it?'

His gaze flickered for an instant, then he shrugged his broad shoulders. 'Nothing,' he said. 'I shouldn't have said it.'

'Why? Because it's not true?'

Again, he shrugged. 'Not exactly. But, all the same, I shouldn't have said it.'

'You're not making any sense.'

'Aren't I?' He smiled a slow smile. 'Well, perhaps it's better that I don't make any sense.' Then, before she could respond, he reached out his hand and softly touched her cheek with the back of his fingers. 'You really do care about your sister, don't you?'

I care a very great deal. She opened her mouth to say it, but somehow only a breathless gasp came out. Her vocal cords seemed to have become paralysed along with the rest of her.

Axel's fingers, the cause of this sudden paralysis, continued, as soft as gossamer to stroke her burning cheek. 'You're quite a girl, you know.' His eyes smiled down at her, and there was a look in them that Katrina had never seen before. 'You're kind-hearted to a fault and impossibly beautiful. How come some man hasn't snapped you up?'

The touch of him was making Katrina's heart shiver. She longed to close her eyes and sink against him. She had to fight to find her voice again. 'What do you mean, some man?' she said.

'Don't your male compatriots recognise quality when they see it?' Soft as velvet, hot as fire, his hand stroked her cheek. 'A prize like you ought to have been snapped up long ago.'

'I don't know what you mean.' Katrina swallowed. 'I'm no prize.'

'Oh, yes, you are.'

With his free hand, very gently, Axel released the empty liqueur glass from her fingers. Which was really just as well, Katrina was thinking. She was clutching it so tightly that there was a very real danger it might suddenly shatter beneath the pressure.

He laid it on the table beside his own and let the hand that a moment ago had been caressing her cheek trickle softly through her hair. 'Do you have a boyfriend?' he wanted to know.

'No. No one serious.' That sounded too obliging. Katrina licked her dry lips and added carefully, 'I used to. Until about a year ago. We'd gone out together since we were at school.'

'And what happened?'

'In the end he married someone else. Someone he'd met while he was on holiday.' As a look crossed Axel's eyes that she suspected might be sympathy, she assured him hurriedly, 'It was the best thing that could have happened. The two of us had been growing apart for years. Habit was really all that kept us together.'

'And there's been no one since?' He looked into her eyes. 'A girl like you... I find that hard to believe.'

'Why?'

'You have to ask why?' He laughed a soft laugh and ran his hand through her hair again. 'Because you're so damned beautiful. Everything about you is beautiful. That gorgeous red hair of yours... those beautiful green eyes... You must have men queueing up to take the place of your old boyfriend.'

'Not quite.'

'I'll bet you do. You're just being modest. Or else the entire male population of Scotland is blind.'

Katrina shook her head and smiled. 'No, I'm not being modest. Red hair and green eyes are ten a penny where I come from. There are lots of girls who look like me.'

'Then you're the one who's blind.' Axel frowned as he smiled down at her. He took a strand of her hair lightly in his fingers and looked at her with such intensity that her heart squeezed inside her. 'In the entire world there's not another girl like you. You, *querida*, are one of a kind.'

Katrina had to glance away from the intensity of that dark gaze and the impossible tumult it had awakened inside her. Her heart was beating so hard that she felt it might explode.

There was a moment of silence. Katrina could feel him breathing softly. Then he said, 'So, there really is no boyfriend?'

She shook her head.

'No one at all?'

'Friends. That's all.'

Katrina glanced up to meet his eyes again. She had a feeling there were some similar questions she ought to be asking him, but she couldn't for the life of her begin to think what they were.

'Good,' Axel observed. 'I'm glad to hear it.'

'I just haven't met anyone I've wanted to get involved with.'

'Choosy, I see?' He smiled as he said it and playfully brushed the end of her nose with her hair.

Katrina blushed to her tingling hair roots and stared hard at his tie again. 'I don't know if I'm choosy,' she only just managed to respond. 'But I'm just not the type who likes to get involved in relationships that I know are destined to come to nothing.'

As she said it, somewhere in the distance a bell rang in her head. But she couldn't think why. She added innocently, 'I see my friends drift in and out of relationships... I'm not saying that's wrong, but it's not what I want.'

'So, you're waiting for Mr Right?'

'I suppose you could say that.' It sounded a little old-fashioned, but essentially it was true. She added, 'Not that I'm in any great hurry for him to come along. I have lots of friends, and my job, to keep me occupied.'

Axel was smiling. 'I told you... you're definitely a one-off.' Then he paused for a moment before knocking the ground from under her. He leaned towards her ever so slightly. 'Spend tomorrow with me,' he suggested. 'I'll take you on a tour of the island. Then we can have dinner together in the evening.'

Was he joking or was he serious? Katrina blinked at him foolishly. She hadn't a clue what she wanted to answer.

Then he increased her confusion by brushing her nose again with the curl of hair he still held in his hand. 'Go on,' he urged her, smiling. 'Say yes.'

Katrina took a deep breath. 'Yes,' she said.

'Good. I'll pick you up at your hotel after breakfast. Ten o'clock. How does that sound?'

It sounded wonderful. Katrina nodded. 'It sounds fine.'

'So, that's settled, then.' He released the strand of hair and let it drop down over her shoulder. 'And now, you must forgive me if I desert you for a

moment. I can see some of my guests are getting
ready to leave, and I'm afraid I've been rather
neglecting them, thanks to you. But don't disappear,' he told her with a quick smile. 'I'll give
you a lift back to the hotel.'

Over the next half-hour or so, all the other guests
left. Katrina bade them farewell in a dreamy kind
of haze, aware of a sense of growing elation, not
caring that she still hadn't pinned down Fergus
Loughlin, who'd departed without giving her any
firm commitment.

Suddenly, all she could think of was this surprise
development. She was going to spend tomorrow
with Axel. And though a part of her kept telling
her this ought not to be happening, another, greater
part of her burned with excitement. Already, she
couldn't wait for tomorrow to come.

'Shall we go?' With the last guest gone, Axel appeared with his car keys. 'Let's get you back to your
hotel for a good night's sleep. Tomorrow,' he
promised, 'is going to be a busy day.'

Then he was leading a delighted, starry-eyed
Katrina down the villa steps to the waiting black
Mercedes.

'Have a think about what you'd like to do
tomorrow.' As they drove the short distance to her
hotel in the centre, he glanced across at her, caught
her eye and winked. 'Tomorrow, for the entire day,
your every wish is my command.'

'OK, I'll have a think.'

Katrina hardly dared to look at him. And it occurred to her that she was in no fit state for
thinking. A fog of blissful rapture had descended
upon her, rendering her incapable of any but the

most basic of brain functions. She was rather hoping the condition might clear up before tomorrow or poor Axel would have a zombie on his hands!

When they reached the hotel, Axel leaned and kissed her cheek. 'Till tomorrow,' he told her, holding her eyes for a moment. And those two words seemed to promise a day of treasures beyond dreams.

Katrina nodded blissfully. 'Till tomorrow,' she breathed.

A couple of minutes later, as she stepped into the hotel lift, she could no longer contain the excitement that gripped her. She threw back her head and let out a whoop of delight.

CHAPTER SIX

IT WAS only once she was in the bathroom, standing before the mirror above the washbasin, taking off her make-up with a pad of cotton wool, that Katrina began to come to her senses.

What was she thinking of, making a date with Axel Jerez—and behaving as though this was the answer to all her dreams? Was she drunk or something? Was she out of her head?

Definitely not the former. She'd had some wine, but not that much, and only a tiny thimbleful of Drambuie. No, she was as sober as a judge. So it must be the latter. Some vital cog in her brain had popped out of its socket.

Katrina stared at her reflection with its one naked eye and the other one still smeared with traces of mascara. You're a clown, she told herself. What are you thinking of? Have you forgotten that he's a married man?

Something plummeted inside her at that timely reminder, but she ignored it as she leaned forward and whisked her clown's eye clean.

He might be separated from his wife, but that made no difference. He was still legally bound to another woman. Sofía had mentioned divorce, but there'd been no divorce yet. And there might never be. He and his wife might get back together.

She dropped the mascara-smeared cotton pad into the waste bin. It had been wrong—and unfair—of him to make overtures to her.

For her part she'd been wrong to accept his invitation—though at the time it had not felt wrong in the slightest. For until just a moment ago, when she had looked at herself in the mirror, the fact that he was married had completely slipped her mind.

How convenient, she chastised herself with a sharp sceptical glance. What about all those warning bells that were ringing in your head? If you'd wanted to, you could have listened to them just a little bit harder!

Well, she was listening to them now and their message was clear enough. They were telling her there was no way she could go through with this date. Absolutely nothing was surer than that.

Katrina slapped on some night cream and went through to the bedroom and stood for a moment, staring down at the phone. It was too late to phone now, but first thing in the morning she would call Axel and tell him their date was off.

She climbed into bed, still feeling edgy but a little better, closed her eyes, emptied her mind and eventually drifted off to sleep.

'Yes? Hello?' Groggily, Katrina raised herself from the pillows and reached for the phone at the side of the bed.

'I didn't wake you, did I? I'm sorry. I apologise. I just wanted to be sure I caught you in time.'

It was Axel—and even in her semi-dormant state, at the sound of his voice, Katrina felt a jolt within her. She sat up with a start, suddenly fully awake.

'It's OK. It doesn't matter.' She glanced quickly at her watch and saw that it was just a little before nine. 'I should have been up ages ago,' she added.

'What for? You're not working today and you were late last night. Why shouldn't you enjoy a nice lie-in?'

Because I was planning to phone you first thing this morning, Katrina answered silently, suddenly remembering. She started to say, 'Look there's something I——' But before she could say more, Axel was cutting in.

'Listen, Katrina... I'm terribly sorry, but I'm afraid I'm going to have to cancel today. Something unexpected's come up. I really do apologise, but there's just no way I can take the day off.'

'That's OK. It doesn't matter in the slightest.'

To her horror she was aware that her voice sounded brittle. She was aware of a suddenly beating pulse in her throat.

'Look, I know it's short notice and I feel really bad about it, but, believe me, Katrina, there's nothing I can do. Let's make it tomorrow. What do you say?'

'I think maybe we shouldn't. I think maybe we shouldn't bother.'

She wanted to sound firm and cool and together. She wanted to tell him that she'd planned to break their date anyway. But suddenly she felt numb with hurt and confusion, and she feared that was precisely the way she sounded, too.

'Look, I'll phone you later.' He was evidently in a hurry. 'Please accept my apologies and enjoy your day.'

Katrina laid down the phone, her stomach churning inside her. She felt sick with horror and rejection and shame. How could she react this way when she hadn't wanted to see him, anyway? How could she let herself down like this? Was she going insane?

She climbed out of bed and headed for the shower, appalled at the way her legs felt shaky beneath her and at how ridiculously close to tears she felt.

Then in the bathroom she glared ferociously at her reflection in the mirror—a picture of hopeless, bleary-eyed misery. Stop it! she told herself. Pull yourself together! Then she switched the shower to 'cold' and stepped determinedly beneath it.

The cold shower helped, and so did a hearty breakfast. And then, just as she was congratulating herself on having regained her senses, the bell boy knocked on Katrina's door to deliver another boost to her spirits.

It was a note from Fergus Loughlin and it read:

It was delightful to make your acquaintance last night and on reconsidering the position I've decided to go ahead with the interview, after all. I can be at your disposal all day Thursday and Friday. Please let my secretary know if this arrangement suits.

Katrina nearly jumped for joy. She picked up the

phone and immediately dialled the number at the top of the note.

'Please tell Mr Loughlin his arrangement suits me perfectly,' she informed his secretary as soon as she was put through. 'And tell him thank you. I'm delighted he's changed his mind.'

She laid down the phone, suddenly in confident high spirits, feeling a great deal more like her usual self again. Today was Tuesday. That gave her a couple of days in hand that she could use to continue her search for Jaime—for, of course, in spite of Axel's suggestion, there was no way she was going to spend tomorrow with him. Not tomorrow nor any other day. She had fully recovered from her madness.

She spent the rest of the day diligently, if unsuccessfully, following up the new leads that Irene had given her. Not a single one of them was able to help her.

She got back to her hotel in the late afternoon and went down to the pool to have a swim. Damn Axel, she told herself, as she did first one length then another one. He's the one I have to thank for this. He's bought them all off.

Yet she'd proven him wrong in her suspicions that he'd bribed Fergus Loughlin, so maybe she was wrong about this as well?

She swam for a while longer, then stretched out on one of the sunbeds and stared through her sunglasses at the huge cloudless sky. She was not wrong, she decided. It had to be Axel who was at the back of this conspiracy of silence. Only he—certainly not Jaime—was capable of wielding such power.

Though why Axel should be so desperate to keep her from Jaime—even to the extent of offering her ten thousand pounds to vanish!—Katrina couldn't begin to imagine. But then a man like Axel didn't need a reason. A man like Axel simply did as he pleased.

And again she thought, a hundred times damn him! For it looked as though on the Jaime front she really was beaten.

That made her feel doubly satisfied with a move she'd made earlier...

This morning Axel had said he'd ring her back later, and no doubt he was assuming she'd be waiting with bated breath. Well, he had a shock in store. For the next couple of days Katrina wouldn't be taking any phone calls. She'd asked the switchboard to take messages—in case Loughlin got in touch—and any messages from Axel would go straight in the bin!

As the sun began to go down, she gathered up her things and headed, finally at peace with herself, back indoors. This evening she would treat herself to dinner at one of the other hotels—since Axel had warned her that hers was a favourite haunt of his! Then she would come back and have that early night she kept promising herself.

Back in her room she showered quickly and phoned down to Room Service for a glass of orange juice. She'd sit out on the balcony for half an hour, drink her orange juice and let her hair dry. She was feeling relaxed and rather looking forward to the quiet little evening she'd planned.

She was giving her hair a quick rub when there was a knock on the door. Wrapping the towel round her head, she hurried to answer it, expecting to find the room service waiter with her orange juice. But what she found was nothing half so pleasant.

'Hi.' With a smile, Axel leaned against the door-frame and flicked a glance at the towel round her head. 'I see I've caught you at an inopportune moment. My apologies—but may I come in?'

'No, you may not!' Katrina's heart was suddenly racing. He was looking, it seemed to her, even more gorgeous than usual, dressed in cream trousers and a blue and white striped shirt. He seemed to radiate an irrestible dark vitality—which, nevertheless, she was determined to resist!

She glared at him and pulled the neck of her cotton robe shut. 'You may very definitely not come in!'

'Why not? I only want to talk to you.' He smiled that dancing smile of his. 'I tried to phone, but I was told you weren't taking any calls.

'That's right, I'm not. And I don't want any visitors. So, I'd be greatly obliged if you'd just go away.'

'Why? Aren't you well?' He cast her a concerned look that surprised her and caused her heart to turn over. 'If you're not feeling well, I hope you've called the hotel doctor? If you haven't, I'll call him for you now.'

'There's no need for that.' Katrina pulled her robe tighter and quickly smothered the warm feeling inside her. He wasn't concerned, he simply enjoyed taking over. Well, he could forget about doing any such thing.

She narrowed her eyes at him. 'I'm feeling perfectly well, thank you. I'm just not feeling very
sociable, that's all.'

'Yes, I can see that.' His own eyes narrowed as
he looked back at her. 'And I suspect I'm probably
to blame for that. Which is all the more reason why
you should let me in—so I can explain and
apologise about today...'

'So you can what? What are you thinking? Are
you thinking I'm upset because you cancelled our
appointment? How utterly preposterous!' Katrina
laughed a harsh laugh. 'I promise you I couldn't
care less about that.'

It was written all over Axel's face what he was
thinking. He was thinking, 'Methinks the lady doth
protest too much.' And her protest, she had to
confess, had definitely sounded a little strident.

Katrina paused, confused, wondering what to say
next. And that was when the waiter from Room
Service appeared.

'Your orange juice, miss.' He hovered by the
doorway, waiting to be allowed in to deliver the
drink.

Automatically, without thinking, Katrina stepped
aside, though even as she did so she knew what
would happen. And she was right. As the waiter
stepped through the doorway, with a smile, Axel
stepped in right behind him, taking as he did so a
banknote from his wallet and handing it to the
waiter.

'Thank you. Keep the change,' he said.

As the waiter withdrew, Katrina turned on Axel
angrily. 'How dare you do that? I was going to sign
for it! You had no business taking over!'

'Pay me back, if you like, if it troubles you so much. But surely the price of an orange juice isn't worth getting so upset about?'

He was right, she sensed, but she reached for her bag anyway, extracted a note and thrust it at him angrily. 'The orange juice was by the way. The real reason I'm angry is because of the way you've come barging into my room!'

He shook his head. 'No, I don't think so. You were already angry before I came barging into your room.' He smiled. 'But I can assure you you won't be angry any more once I've had a chance to explain.'

So, he was still insisting that she was upset because of their cancelled date! Katrina tossed her head at him. 'Don't waste your breath,' she told him. 'I couldn't care less about your apologies and explanations.'

Quite clearly, he did not believe her. 'You have every reason to be angry. But I promise you the only reason I broke our date was because I had absolutely no choice in the matter.'

'Axel Jerez having no choice? I really can't believe it!' She had intended it to come out sounding detached and scathing, but to her dismay her tone was resentful and accusing. 'That'll be the day!' she added, making matters worse.

'You flatter me.' He smiled and seated himself unhurriedly on the arm of the armchair that stood by the window. 'I'm really not as ominipotent as you seem to think.'

'I never thought you were omnipotent.' Her eyes flashed angrily, as though they would uproot him from the chair arm. 'It's just that I happen to have great difficulty seeing you as an innocent, helpless victim of circumstance.'

'Nevertheless, sometimes I am.' His eyes flickered amusedly. 'And today, I'm afraid, was one of those occasions.'

'So, what happened?'

'A family crisis.'

'A family crisis?' she repeated.

His wife, she was thinking, and felt suddenly sick.

'I'd explain more fully if I could, but I can't, I'm afraid. However, it was a real crisis. You can take my word for that.'

'I'm sure it was.' She felt numb all over. That airy, obscure reference to his marital problems, to her dismay, had felt like a physical blow. She pulled herself up and observed in a cool tone, 'It's only right. People who are involved in family crises really can't be expected to think of other things.'

'I'm glad you understand.'

'Oh, I understand all right.'

As she looked at him, she longed to say straight out that she knew about his wife and the break-up of his marriage. But her instinct held her back. Hadn't he told her at the beginning that he never discussed his private life? He would not take kindly to such a comment. But she could not resist an oblique allusion.

Feeling her heart thump strangely, she observed in a careful tone, 'In fact, one might say that people who are involved in family crises really have no business thinking of other things.'

She saw a look cross his face. Had he understood, she wondered, what she had really meant by that remark?

He let a moment go by, then he said, one eyebrow lifted, 'Even in the most difficult of family crises one has to think of other things. And I was sorry to break our date. I was looking forward to it very much.'

There was a sincere look in his eyes that made her heart squeeze tightly. She felt oddly torn between a feeling of simple pleasure at the patent honesty of the compliment he'd just paid her and a sense of regret that he had no right to pay such compliments. Suddenly, she was feeling all tangled up inside.

'So, do you forgive me?'

'For breaking our appointment?'

Katrina found herself glancing away as she answered and deliberately avoided using the word date—though he'd used it, several times, as though nothing could be more natural.

He seemed so unaffected, it occurred to her, by the break-up of his marriage, as though it was something he'd already put behind him. She remembered the way he'd looked that time she'd seen him in the car, with his face turned stonily against his angry wife. Quite clearly, he doesn't love her, she found herself thinking, and was shocked at the feeling of satisfaction that brought.

'You still haven't answered my question, *querida*. I'm still waiting to hear if you forgive me.'

'There's nothing to forgive. You were simply doing what you had to do.' His wife had obviously been making waves again. She glanced up as he spoke and met his eyes unexpectedly, those deep dark eyes as mysterious as moonbeams. And in that instant she felt her stomach disappear.

She was still fighting the feeling when he suddenly took a step towards her and reached out to cup her chin with his fingers. 'Now that we've cleared that up, kindly go and get dressed. I've come here to take you out to dinner.'

Katrina jolted at the touch of him, her skin on fire beneath his fingers. She wanted to step away, but she could not move a muscle. It was as though he had nailed her feet to the floor.

She just managed to say, 'I'm not free for dinner. I'm afraid I've already made other arrangements.'

'Who with?' He frowned down at her, almost disapproving. Then his expression relaxed. 'With Fergus Loughlin?'

'No, not with Fergus.'

Again he frowned. 'Then who?'

'No one. I was planning to have dinner on my own. And I fully intend to go ahead with that plan.'

'You can go ahead with it some other time. Tonight you're dining with me.' Axel tilted her chin with his long brown fingers so that she had no choice but to look into his face. 'I'll wait downstairs. Be ready in half an hour.'

Then he released her and headed with a smile for the door, pausing only to advise her over his shoulder,

'Don't forget to take the towel off your head. I want the full benefit of that glorious head of hair.'

The minute he was gone Katrina snatched off the towel and, venting her frustration, flung it down on the floor. She didn't want to have dinner with him—and yet she knew she really did. Frankly, she

didn't know what was going on inside her own head
any more!

She sank down on to the bed and tried to con-
centrate her thoughts. Perhaps she was taking this
all a little too seriously. All he had done was invite
her to dinner, after all. What could be more
harmless than that?

With a wry frown she glanced at her reflection
in the wall mirror. Don't lie to yourself, she told
herself. It's not the dinner you're worried about.
It's the way he makes you feel. It's the way you're
afraid one thing might lead to another. What you're
worried about is the fact that he's married.

She glanced away at that thought, then forced
herself to look back again. Face it, she told herself.
Face the fact that he's married. Face the fact that
he's strictly out of bounds, even if he is currently
separated from his wife. And face the fact that you
have to get control of your feelings and stop reacting
to him the way you do.

Straight-backed, firm-chinned, she rose from the
bed and walked on resolute steps to the wardrobe.
Simply think of him as the brother of your sister's
ex-boyfriend, someone you can't help having
dealings with if you're going to track down Jaime.

With a sigh she slid from its hanger a demure
emerald two-piece with a high round neck and
below-the-knee skirt and laid it in readiness on the
bed. Then she went through to the bathroom and
quickly dried her hair, briefly toying with the idea
of wearing it pinned up tonight.

But she decided against it. She never quite felt
herself with her hair up, and this evening she definitely wanted to feel like herself—like the sensible,

level-headed Katrina MacGregor who would never
dream of looking at another woman's man. Which
was what Axel Jerez was, after all.

She slipped her feet into a pair of strappy green
sandals and dropped her lipstick and a few pesetas
into her black evening clutch bag. I shall use this
evening, she told herself firmly, to find out what I
can about Jaime's whereabouts. Nothing more intimate will pass between us.

Then with a last determined glance at her reflection in the mirror, she turned on her heel and
headed for the door.

So much for the theory, she thought. Now let's
see if I can put it into practice!

Axel took her to a restaurant down by the marina,
a friendly little place with candlelit tables and
fishing nets and anchors hanging from the walls
and ceiling.

'I hope you like fish?' he had asked her in the
car. 'I know a place where they serve some of the
best fish on the island.'

'I love fish,' she'd told him.

'Then that's where we'll go.'

And now they were seated at a table by the
window with a spectacular view out over the whispering moonlit sea. Katrina was studying the huge
menu the waiter had handed her. She glanced up
at Axel and shook her head at him. 'I like the sound
of everything. It's impossible to choose.'

He smiled across the table at her. 'Then have a
bit of everything. I'll ask the waiter to put together
a special concoction.'

'That sounds terrific.'

'Then consider it done.' He winked across at her.
'Your wish is my command.'

Katrina sat back in her seat, distancing herself
from him. In the glow of the candlelight he seemed
far too alluring, dark eyes flickering and dancing
with secret promises. When he had winked, she had
felt her heart twist inside her. And such feelings
were not feelings she had any wish to feel.

She threw him a shrewd look. 'One thing I'm
wondering...why have you invited me out to
dinner?' Just to let him know she deemed an
explanation necessary.

Axel also sat back, regarding her through his
lashes, a smile of amusement on his lips. 'For the
simple pleasure of your company,' he answered.
'What man wouldn't enjoy dining with a beautiful
girl like you?'

Flattery would get him nowhere. A frown
touched Katrina's brow as she reflected that she was
probably seeing the reason for his marriage
breakdown. A man like Axel would be incapable
of being faithful.

She fiddled with her fork as she glanced across
at him. 'I just wondered,' she said. 'I mean, considering the situation...' She held his gaze, speaking
volumes with her eyes. 'Some might think this little
dinner of ours less than appropriate.'

The flicker of a frown crossed his eyes for a
moment. Then he said, looking straight at her,
'Then why are you here?'

'Perhaps I'm hoping to pick your brains.' She
regarded him candidly. 'After all, as you know, I'm
still trying to find Jaime.'

'Ah, Jaime...' For an instant his expression altered. A shadow seemed to fall across his eyes. Then he said, 'Sorry, Jaime's not on the conversational agenda. We can talk about anything you like, but not my brother.'

Then he smiled, one of those quick, disarming smiles he was so good at. 'For example, I'd rather like to talk about you.' Then before she could say a word, he threw her another wink. 'But, first, I think we ought to order.'

At least as far as the food was concerned, Katrina had no complaints. Axel ordered the promised mixed dish of seafood for her—a selection of just about everything on the menu. The waiter laid it before her with a delighted flourish. '*Para la linda señorita pelirroja*!' he proclaimed.

'What did he say?' As Axel smiled in response, she detached her amazed gaze from the platter before her and glanced at him curiously across the table. 'And why are you smiling so broadly?' she added.

'He called you the beautiful red-haired *señorita*— precisely my own feelings, as you know. And I was smiling,' he added, 'at the look on your face when he laid that plate down on the table in front of you. You looked as though you'd never seen anything like it in your life.'

'I haven't!' Katrina laughed. 'And I'm never going to be able to finish it! There's more here than I normally eat in a week!'

'You'll finish it, don't worry. We have all evening. And you can rest between mouthfuls and tell me all about yourself.' He held her eyes. 'I think that was the subject we agreed on.'

'We agreed on no such thing.' Yet Katrina smiled as she said it. She felt relaxed and at ease. Axel was behaving with perfect decorum. She had nothing to worry about. This was just an innocent dinner.

And in the event, to her own surprise, she did end up talking quite a lot about herself—about her schooldays and her family and the area where she was brought up.

'So, your father's an engineer. A very Scottish occupation.' Axel smiled with genuine interest across the table. 'What a pity, though, that his own business didn't succeed.'

'It was a tragedy at the time. It almost broke him.' Katrina found it surprisingly easy to tell him such things, things that normally she never discussed with anyone. 'But he got over it. He's happy now. He's got a good job with a local company.'

In return Axel told her quite a lot about himself— though not a word about his marriage! It was as though it didn't exist for him, Katrina found herself pondering, smothering the comforting effect that thought had on her. But it does exist, she reminded herself sharply.

He seemed happy enough, however, to talk about his childhood and his initial forays into business.

'The first hotel I ever bought was a run-down little place. Everyone told me I was mad, that I was throwing away my money. But I proved them wrong. Within a year it was making a profit. Which was just as well, because by then I'd acquired two more!'

Katrina laughed. 'By now I suppose you've lost count of all the hotels and things you own?'

'No, I haven't lost count. In fact, I keep count very carefully.' An unexpectedly sentimental look crossed his eyes. 'One day I'll have a son or daughter to hand them on to. For their sake, if nothing else, I have to keep a careful tally.'

'One day...' Katrina held her breath as she looked across at him. So she had learned at least one important personal detail. He and his wife had no children. 'You said one day,' she repeated. 'That sounds like a long way in the future.'

He smiled. 'Well, I have no plans to embark on fatherhood at the moment. First, I have to find the right woman to be their mother.'

'You mean you haven't found her?'

Discreetly, she was fishing. You're not planning on a reconciliation, then? was what she was really asking.

A thoughtful look crossed his face. 'There was a time when I thought I'd found her, but then I discovered I'd been wrong.' He smiled a quick smile. 'You're not the only one who makes mistakes.'

So, it was definitely all over. That seemed pretty clear. Katrina was aware of a shameful little lift inside her. In a way, one could almost argue he was scarcely married at all.

The conversation grew more general. They talked about books and films and holidays, and the time passed so quickly that Katrina was amazed when she glanced round the previously crowded restaurant to discover they were virtually the only people left. She frowned down at her watch and saw that it was long after midnight.

'Good grief!' she exclaimed. 'I had no idea!'

'I think maybe we ought to go.' Axel beckoned
to the waiter and indicated that he was ready to pay
the bill. 'We're keeping the poor restaurant staff
out of their beds.'

Katrina nodded. He was right. But she felt
reluctant all the same to end what had turned out
to be an enchanting evening. Over the past few
hours she felt she had grown to know him. And
she really rather liked what she had grown to know.
It was sad that the evening was destined never to
be repeated.

It was as they were driving back to her hotel that
Axel surprised her. He turned towards her. 'We were
supposed to be spending a day together. What about
tomorrow, since we didn't make it today?'

With all her heart Katrina wanted to say yes. But,
without even looking at him, she answered, 'I don't
think so.'

He said nothing for a few minutes. Then, as they
were drawing up outside the hotel, he remarked, 'I
hear Fergus has relented. He phoned to tell me he's
seeing you on Thursday. Congratulations. I knew
you'd win him round.'

'Thanks.'

Katrina stared intently down into her lap, feeling
her heart roaring and clattering inside her. She
wanted to linger with him, yet she wanted to flee.
It was hopeless. Her brain seemed to be tied up in
knots.

There was a silence. She was aware of him
shifting in his seat. She could feel the dark eyes
focused on her face.

Then he spoke. 'Are you sure you won't change
your mind about tomorrow?'

Katrina shook her head. 'No. I can't.' Her voice wobbled.

'It's just a friendly invitation. I'd like to show you the island. We could have lunch somewhere together—and I promise I wouldn't eat you.'

It was the smile in his voice that made her glance up, and as soon as she did she knew she shouldn't have. It was like toppling off a cliff into the darkness of his eyes. She felt as though he had reached out and taken hold of her.

And then he did and her heart grew still within her. Suddenly, she was frozen, unable to breathe.

He had taken hold of her hand, though only very gently, and equally gently he was looking into her eyes. 'Look, I know you're not the type of girl who goes in for casual relationships. You already told me that and I believe you. But I'm not looking for something casual. I just want you to know that. You're special, Katrina. Very special.'

Making her heart skip a beat, he raised her hand to his lips and kissed it. 'Think about tomorrow. I'll be at home all morning. If you change your mind, just come any time. And if you come early enough, we can have breakfast together.'

Then he dropped her hand. 'Goodnight, Katrina. And thank you for the best evening I've had in a long time.'

It was only as she was climbing into bed, her eyes still dreamy with the magic of the evening, that Katrina suddenly realised she'd left her bag in Axel's car.

She sighed and frowned. Now I have no choice.
I'll have to go to the villa tomorrow morning to
fetch it.

With a smile of contentment, she slid between
the sheets. It looked as though fate was coming to
her aid!

Katrina woke early after a deep and dreamless sleep,
still feeling as though she was floating on a cloud.
But, all the same, as she stepped beneath the
shower, she reviewed her decision of the previous
night.

Would it be wise to go to the villa, she asked
herself over and over, even if ostensibly just to pick
up her bag? After all, if it was really just the bag
she cared about, she could always phone and ask
Axel to drop it over. If she went, he would know
she had accepted his invitation.

But it had been such a special invitation, how
could she refuse it? Clearly, after all, he cared for
her a little and had no intention of luring her into
some shabby affair.

He respected her. He'd as good as said that. He
was not playing some game with her. And it was
plain that his relationship with his wife was over
and that in effect he was married only in name.
And the marriage itself was soon to be ended.

She dressed carefully and quickly in a simple skirt
and top, then went downstairs and caught a taxi. I
ought to be in time for breakfast, she was thinking,
as she sat back in her seat, grinning from ear to
ear.

Her smile never slipped throughout the brief
journey. In fact, it seemed to Katrina, it simply grew

broader. She felt drunk with anticipation, over-
joyed at the thought of seeing him—and of seeing
again the look she had seen in his eyes last night.
Every time she thought of it her heart beat a little
faster.

It was beating like a drum as they turned into
the villa grounds and her smile, if that was possible,
was even broader. It was only as the cab stopped
and she stepped down on to the gravel driveway
that, with a crash, the smile slipped from her face.

For beyond the trees, at the far end of the garden,
suddenly she had caught sight of Axel.

He hadn't noticed her, and the reason for that
was simple. Every ounce of his attention appeared
to be focused on the blonde-haired woman who was
walking at his side and around whose waist his arm
was wrapped as though it had been wrapped there
many times before.

Katrina stared at them, stiff with horror and dis-
belief. For pity's sake, how many women did Axel
have in his life? And who was this one? Was this
his girlfriend?

It certainly looked that way. She was definitely
no stranger. He's disgusting, she thought savagely.
A philandering, immoral beast!

Pale as a sheet, she stumbled back inside the taxi.
She leaned towards the driver. 'Get me out of here!'
she croaked.

CHAPTER SEVEN

KATRINA stared blindly out of the window as the taxi headed back to Santa Cruz. She felt sick and numb and terribly angry.

How could Axel have come on to her like that last night, lying to her and telling her she was special, when clearly all she really was was another notch in his belt? For she had just seen with her own eyes that he already had a girlfriend.

A wave of jealousy washed over her, making her shiver. It was unbearable the way she felt each time she recalled the sight of his arm wrapped round that blonde woman's waist.

Yet it should scarcely surprise her that he had a girlfriend. Hadn't she always suspected he was a philanderer? And it explained why he seemed so unconcerned about the break-up of his marriage. He was already involved with someone else!

At last they'd reached the hotel. Katrina stumbled from the taxi, fumbling in her purse for change. Suddenly she was all thumbs. She barely knew what she was doing. It was an effort just to stand up straight and breathe.

She took the lift to her room and closed the door behind her, slipping the security chain into place. Suddenly, all she wanted was to lock the world out, to shut herself up in her safe little sanctuary where nothing and nobody could touch her.

Dropping her purse on a chair, she stared at the bed, resisting the urge to throw herself on it. To do that would be fatal, the ultimate weakness. For, if she were to do that, she knew the tears would start. And there must be no tears. He wasn't worth her tears.

She breathed deeply and slowly, staring at nothing, fighting back the threatening well of misery inside her. She had no reason to feel miserable. She had no reason to feel anything—anything, that was, except cheated and angry.

And it was at that moment, as she forced herself to focus on her anger, that the phone beside the bed began to ring.

'Who is it? I'm not here! I'm not taking any calls!' Driven by her anger she had snatched up the phone. 'Is it too much to ask to be left in peace?' she snapped.

'It's me. I'm downstairs. Come down at once. And I mean at once. I want to talk to you.'

At the sound of Axel's voice, Katrina felt her blood freeze. So, after all, he had witnessed her flight from the villa and knew that she had seen him with his girlfriend.

So, what did he want with her? She longed to slam the phone down, but she forced herself to say, 'I'm not coming down. So, kindly just go away. I have nothing to say to you.'

'Perhaps not, but I have plenty to say to you.'

'That's too bad. I'm not interested in hearing it.'

She heard him sigh, a sharp sound of impatience. 'Look, let's not have this same old conversation all over again. If you don't come down,

I'll come up. You have five minutes.' And with that the phone went dead.

Katrina swore and banged the receiver down on its cradle. 'I will not go down!' she vowed out loud. 'I will not do as he says. Just let him try and make me!'

Then she glared at the door. If he came, she would ignore him. Let him rant and rave and cause a commotion. She would die before she'd let him into her room.

But even as she scowled and glowered her defiance, a sudden thought made her stop short and wonder.

Why was she making such a drama out of this? Why was she behaving as though she really cared? She'd been momentarily shocked, but no more than that, surely? There was no need to act as though it was a tragedy. And there was absolutely no reason why she shouldn't confront him.

She straightened. In fact, there was every reason why she should. He probably thought she was lying prostrate on the bed, the very thing she'd refused to allow herself to do!

Shaking back her hair, she glanced in the mirror and gave her pale cheeks a quick pinch with her fingers. I'll show him! she told herself, green eyes sparking. I'll show him it's not so easy to throw Katrina MacGregor!

A minute later, with an air of serene, unruffled calm, she was taking the lift down to the lobby. But as she stepped out and saw Axel walking towards her, it took every last ounce of her iron control not to betray the sudden thrust of emotion that went through her.

He's lost to me, she thought. He always was lost. And though she tried to remind herself that he wasn't worth having, it still felt like a terrible, tragic thing.

She banished these feelings as he came to stand before her. 'Well,' he said. 'So you decided to come down?'

'So it would seem.' She forced herself to speak calmly. She even managed an accompanying ironical little smile. 'Though, as I said before, I really can't see the point of this. I can't see what you could possibly have to say to me.'

'Then, no doubt, you'll be interested to find out.' He glanced towards the doors that led out on to the terrace where small clusters of tables were informally arranged. 'I suggest we sit outside. I'm going to have breakfast. You can join me, unless you've already eaten.'

Katrina hadn't eaten, of course, and quite frankly she wasn't hungry. All her recent emotional upheavals had rather squashed her appetite. But she responded with a shrug. 'Yes, let's have breakfast.' She'd be damned if she'd let him know he'd affected her appetite!

Axel led her outside to a table in a quiet corner— he evidently preferred to spin his lies in privacy, or perhaps feared an emotional outburst from her.

Katrina seated herself with a composed smile. He had no need to fear an outburst. All he would get from her from was indifference and cold contempt.

Not a word was exchanged until the waiter had taken their order. Then as the man hurried off, Axel slipped from his jacket pocket her black clutch bag and laid it on the table before her.

'You left this in the car last night,' he said.

'Yes, I know.' She flicked a brief glance at the bag, whose existence until that moment she had entirely forgotten. 'It was in order to retrieve it that I came by your house.'

'Then why did you leave without it?' He fixed her with a dark look. 'That strikes me as rather a strange thing to do.'

'I had my reasons.' She looked at him coldly. 'But I don't see why I need explain them to you.'

'I rather thought you'd want to. You see, it seems very odd that you would go flying off so dramatically like that just because you saw me walking in the garden with a woman.'

'A woman?' Katrina remembered the intimate way they'd been walking and had to fight against the way her stomach tightened in jealous misery. She sat back in her seat and narrowed her eyes at him. 'Are you trying to tell me,' she accused him, 'that she was just a woman?'

'Why, who do you think she was?'

'I think she was more than just a woman.' She glared at him accusingly, calling his bluff. For the moment she would refrain from using the world 'girlfriend'. If he had any decency at all, let him admit the truth himself.

She exhaled disapprovingly and demanded, 'Why don't *you* tell me who she was?'

'OK. I'll tell you.' He was sitting back in his chair, watching her unblinkingly through expressionless jet-black eyes. Then he smiled suddenly. 'The woman you saw me with happened to be my sister-in-law, Maria.'

'Your sister-in-law?'

Katrina blinked at him, not quite certain if she believed him. Though it could be true, she thought with a spurt of optimism. He had two other brothers besides Jaime.

She shifted in her seat. 'You seem to be on good terms with your sister-in-law.'

The way his arm had been wrapped round the blonde woman's waist had appeared just a touch too intimate, she thought.

'You're right, I'm on very good terms with Maria.' Axel paused and held her eyes for a moment, and suddenly his expression had grown clouded and serious. Then he continued, 'But not the sort of good terms you're thinking. Maria is very ill. She can't walk without support.'

'That woman is ill?'

Katrina blinked at him guiltily. She could see in his eyes that he was telling her the truth. And though she knew it was disgraceful, suddenly all she could think of was how relieved she was that there was no girlfriend, after all.

But then as the tension in her slackened, she forgot about herself and responded to the cloudy look that still shadowed Axel's eyes.

She leaned towards him. 'I'm sorry,' she said. 'What's wrong with her? She looked too young to be ill.'

'Yes, she is too young.' There was a catch in his voice. He paused for a moment, taking hold of his emotions. 'She has a rare, untreatable form of leukaemia and I'm afraid it's killing her very fast.'

'That's terrible.' Katrina felt a rush of sadness go through her. She leaned across the table, her

green eyes filled with sympathy. 'I really am dread-
fully sorry,' she said.

'Thank you. That's kind.' Axel nodded briefly.
Then he glanced down for a moment or two at the
table. 'That was the crisis yesterday that kept me
from meeting you. She had a sudden bad turn and
I had to go to the hospital. Unfortunately, my
brother couldn't be there. But she came through it
and by the evening she was sitting up in bed again.'

He sighed and shook his head. 'She insisted on
being released from the hospital, just for the
evening and overnight. So I took her to my place
and returned her to the hospital this morning.'

'So, she doesn't stay at home, then? I mean she's
hospitalised for the most part?'

'Yes. She has been for over a year.'

'And the hospital allows her to come and go as
she pleases?'

'More or less. When she's able. They'd have a
job trying to stop her.' He smiled an affectionate
smile, full of pride and admiration. 'Maria is a
brave and very determined lady, and as she says,
what has she to lose? Her occasional breaks from
the hospital mean a very great deal to her. They
boost her spirits and stop her getting too depressed.'

'Then she's right to insist on being released when
she wants. She's right to make the most of what's
left of her life.'

Katrina looked into Axel's eyes and just for a
moment a sudden fierce sympathy passed between
them. He's a good man, Katrina thought. He clearly
loves his sister-in-law dearly and is taking her illness
pretty hard. She longed to reach out and lay a comforting hand on his arm.

The waiter chose that moment to appear with their breakfasts. And Katrina was glad. It gave her a moment to gather herself. Her feelings of sympathy were best left unexpressed. There was too much danger of them turning into something else.

There was a silence as the waiter laid out their things—orange juice, a pot of coffee, a basket of croissants and some strawberry jam. Then at last he moved away, leaving them alone again.

Axel spoke first. 'So, now you know,' he said, 'what I was up to when you saw me. All perfectly innocent. Not worth getting so upset about.' He winked at her and calmly took a mouthful of his orange juice.

Katrina felt herself blush. She was feeling hopelessly vulnerable, not certain at all how she ought to react.

It seemed that, thankfully, she'd been wrong. He was not a philanderer. And just knowing that alone filled her heart with hope and joy. But there was still so much he hadn't made clear to her.

What were his feelings for her? Was his marriage really over? She was still in the dark about so many things. She frowned to herself. He hadn't even admitted he was married!

But the subject had to be broached. Katrina picked up her orange juice and stared down at it for a moment, gathering her courage. Then she raised her eyes to his and observed in an even tone, 'You know, that wasn't the first time I'd seen you with a woman. And the other time it definitely wasn't your sister-in-law.'

He looked confused for a moment. The dark eyes frowned at her. 'What other time are you talking about?' he demanded.

Katrina drank before answering. Her heart was pounding like a cannon. With stiff, tight fingers she laid her glass down.

'I saw you in the city centre once. You were in your car. And you were having a row with a dark-haired woman in a yellow dress.'

A shadow touched his eyes. Axel leaned back in his chair. Then he assumed an air of nonchalance. 'You saw us?' he enquired.

The pounding with every second was growing louder. There was something about his attitude that was making her heart quake.

'I was in a café nearby. I saw the whole thing.'

'How unfortunate. It was rather an ugly little scene.'

Katrina swallowed drily and watched as he glanced away. She had no idea how she'd expected this conversation to go, but she had not expected it to go like this.

She'd been hoping he'd just be straight with her, but he was being oddly evasive. As she watched him, she felt a sudden lick of fear.

Then he said, 'Do you know who that woman was?'

'Of course I know.'

Her heart flared inside her.

'And do you know why she was so upset?'

'Yes, I know that, too.'

Again her heart flared. Why was he playing this foolish guessing game with her? And why, in spite of his outward calm, did he suddenly seem so hostile? For she could feel a barrier like an iron-spiked wall between them.

And suddenly the fear in her was so real she could have taken it and held it in the palm of her hand.

But she refused to turn back. She forced herself to say, 'The break-up of a marriage is a terribly sad thing. I'm not the least bit surprised she was upset.'

Axel looked at her in silence as a moment stretched into infinity. The muscles above his cheekbones had tensed. Then he drew in his breath and expelled it very slowly.

'Sofía...!' he said, making it sound like an oath.

Katrina could not deny that it was indeed Sofía who had told her everything the other evening at the dinner party. But she was swift to defend her innocent informant.

'She only told me because I brought up the subject. And I can assure you she didn't go into any details.'

'That was very decent of her.' The words cut like a razor. Clearly, he was furious at having his private life revealed.

Katrina felt suddenly guilty for betraying Sofía. She frowned across at him and attempted to appease him. 'She didn't really say much. Just that she was terribly sorry.'

'Not as sorry as I am that she went gabbing to you.' Again his tone was like the slash of a razor. 'I suppose she told you about the impending divorce?' He reached for the coffee-pot and splashed coffee into his cup, violently, as though he was taking his rage out on the china.

Then he banged the coffee-pot down. 'Well, there's not going to be a divorce! Not if I have anything to do with it!'

In the moments that followed the silence was deafening. Katrina stared at him numbly. She could not speak. She could not move. But at last she knew the nature of the fear that had been closing in on her right from the start of this conversation. It stood before her, revealed, its fangs bloodied and bared.

There was to be no divorce. Axel still loved his wife.

Katrina looked into his face and felt her insides fall apart.

It seemed as they sat there in silence a lifetime ticked by. Then, apparently recovered, Axel reached for his coffee-cup and Katrina forced herself to blink the mist from her eyes. If she were to survive the next few minutes, she must push aside her pain and focus hard on something else.

She took a deep breath. 'Good,' she said drily, firming her shoulders, pulling herself up in her chair. Then as he glanced at her through eyes that were still as sharp as rapiers, she added in a remarkably controlled tone of voice, considering the tumult in her heart,

'While we're on the subject of such things, I'd just like to ask you to kindly refrain from making any more sexual advances. I don't like it. In fact, I find it quite insulting.'

Just for a fleeting moment he looked surprised by her change of tack. Then he shrugged. 'I wasn't insulting you. Quite the opposite.' As he said it, he actually had the brass neck to smile. 'I don't make sexual advances to women I wish to insult. Only to women I wish to flatter.'

Katrina glared at him. 'Well, I'm sorry, but I don't feel flattered.'

Their eyes met and held across the barely touched breakfast table. And there was a defiant look in his that caused her to add angrily, 'In fact I find your behaviour quite disgusting.'

'More disgust, I see?'

She ignored that and added flintily. 'So, in future, kindly remember what I've just said.'

'I'll certainly do my best. Though I confess, it won't be easy. After all, I know what I'm missing.'

His arrogance and lack of caring were deeply hurtful. If only he could have just apologised for misleading her, Katrina was thinking. But instead he was deliberately continuing to insult her.

She glared at him, her heart breaking. 'And what is that supposed to mean?'

'Oh, nothing much.' One dark eyebrow lifted. Then his eyes swam over her, stripping her naked. 'It's just that I can remember what that famous disgust of yours feels like when you allow yourself to give it free rein...'

He smiled. 'Over the years I've been kissed many times by many different girls in many different ways, but I have never before in all my life been kissed quite as thoroughly as I was kissed by you.'

Katrina sprang to her feet. She wanted to weep from pain and anger. 'How dare you?' she protested. 'How dare you say that? You philanderer! You're just like your brother! You disgust me!'

'So you keep saying.' With an unrepentant smile and quite unhurriedly, Axel rose to his feet. Then he said in a low voice, stepping towards her, 'But, as I've already told you, disgust is not an emotion I have ever sensed in you. I've sensed plenty of others, but, alas, not disgust.'

He reached out almost idly to catch a strand of her hair and let it curl softly round his finger. Then, very deliberately, he met her eyes and added, 'You really do cover it up extremely well.'

Katrina slapped his hand away. 'Get your hands off me!' She was surprised she'd found the strength to do it, for, as always when he touched her, all her limbs seemed to have become paralysed. Then she flared at him angrily, 'Why don't you just go?'

'I was just about to, *señorita*. Have no fear.' And it seemed he was indeed about to step away. But instead, shocking her totally, he leaned towards her and, with a wicked, taunting smile, bent to kiss her on the lips.

In the same instant he had caught her hand before it could make contact with his face. He smiled at her tauntingly. 'Just testing,' he said.

Then he was turning arrogantly on his heel and heading back into the hotel.

Katrina watched him go, throbbing with anger. That kiss had been the final, crushing insult. She clenched her fists, blinking back tears of hurt and rage, hating him as she had never hated anyone before.

And that was probably why the accident happened. As, stiff-legged, she strode back across the terrace, heading for the hotel lobby and the lift to her room, her mind was so filled with her anger and outrage that she was paying scarcely any attention to what was happening around her.

The real fault, however, was with the other guest, as he came barging through the glass doors, not looking where he was going. In other circumstances Katrina would have seen him in time and moved out of the way before he crashed into her. But, as it was, she didn't. The next thing she knew she was hurtling to the ground, her head cracking against the paving stones.

An instant later the world went black.

And then Katrina had the most extraordinary hallucination. It seemed to her that Axel was bending over her, his dark handsome face full of compassion and tenderness. Through the coldness that suddenly filled her she felt a flicker of warmth. And then, just as she was about to smile at him, everything once again went black.

CHAPTER EIGHT

'How do you feel? Does your head hurt?'

Katrina blinked herself out of the stupor that possessed her and made an effort to focus on the face that was bent over her. So, it wasn't a hallucination, after all, she thought dreamily. For the face bent over her was Axel's.

She glanced confusedly round the room where she lay. 'Where am I?' she demanded thickly.

'You're in hospital,' Axel told her. 'But don't worry,' he added quickly, as a frown of anxiety touched her forehead. 'You're perfectly all right, apart from a bump on the head. By this evening you'll be feeling as right as rain again.'

'But why am I here if there's nothing wrong with me?' Katrina was suddenly aware of the antiseptic hospital smells and of the crispness of the sheets on the bed in which she lay. 'How long have I been here?' she asked, her anxiety stirring again.

'A couple of hours. I brought you here and waited while they took you to X-ray. But the X-ray was clean. The damage is only superficial.'

As Axel spoke, very gently, he stroked her hand with his fingers. Katrina glanced down at her hand, which was held lightly in his, and wondered fleetingly if she ought to withdraw it.

But she decided against it and left it where it was. The way he was stroking her was deeply soothing,

145

and there was nothing even remotely sexual about
it. He might have been stroking an injured puppy!

She relaxed back against her pillows as he continued, 'You have mild concussion and, as I already
told you, a rather nasty bump on your head.' His
eyes fixed on the spot, just above her temple, where
Katrina was aware of a delicate throbbing. 'Fortunately, you didn't need any stitches.' He smiled.
'So in a few days you'll be as beautiful as ever
again.'

With her free hand Katrina reached up to feel
the bump and encountered a wadge of tape-secured
bandage. She smiled. 'What a fright I must look.'
Then her expression grew serious again. 'Did you
say *you* brought me here? That was very good of
you.'

'It was the least I could do. I more or less saw
the accident happen. And since my car was right
outside, I just brought you straight here.' He smiled
down at her. 'But I don't think you were aware of
any of that.'

'Not really.' Yet she felt a blush touch her cheeks
as she remembered the warm feeling that had gone
pouring through her when she had resurfaced momentarily to see him bending over her. His eyes then
had been filled with a look of such concern that
she had felt kissed by a glow of radiant happiness.
And, even now, she could see a lingering shadow
of that look.

Axel continued to watch her. 'You fell with such
a crash that I thought you must have split your head
wide open.' He shook his head. 'That clumsy idiot,
barging through the door without even looking
where he was going.' He muttered something in

Spanish. 'I gave him a piece of my mind, I'll tell you.'

Katrina smiled back at him, feeling a foolish flush of pleasure. My handsome, gallant saviour and protector, she was thinking, as she looked up in warm delight into his face.

Then, instantly dropping her eyes away, she reminded herself briskly—handsome, gallant, *married* saviour and protector. Pretending to adjust the bedclothes, she slipped her hand free from his.

Then she told him in a detached tone, 'I hope you weren't too hard on him. After all, it was an accident.'

'Don't worry, he's still in one piece—*just,*' Axel added, winking. Then as she smiled, he nodded to the table by the bed. 'In fact, he sent you these to say he's sorry.'

Katrina had barely noticed the vases of flowers by her bed. 'All of them?' she blinked, swivelling round to look at them. For there were three vases in all, each packed with colourful blooms. She had rarely seen such a glorious display.

'No, not all of them. Just one of them,' Axel explained now. 'One of them is from the management of the hotel—who also, incidentally, have insisted on paying your hospital bill.'

'But they don't have to do that. I'm insured—at least I think I am.'

'Well, they're insisting anyway, so just be gracious and accept it. They don't like accidents happening to their guests.'

'Well, I must say that's very decent of them. In that case I'll accept.' Katrina turned with a smile to glance again at the flowers. 'My assailant and

the hotel ... that accounts for two of the vases ...
But there are three vases here. Who's the other one
from?'

'The other one's from me.'

'From you. That wasn't necessary.' Again, to her
dismay, Katrina felt a warm flush of pleasure.
'You've already done enough—for which I'm
extremely grateful. You really didn't have to buy
me flowers as well.'

'I wanted to... and they come with a double
message.' He paused for a moment, the dark eyes
thoughtful and serious. 'One is a simple get-well
message. And the other...'

Again he paused, letting his eyes drift over her,
making the hairs on the back of her neck bristle
and tingle. Katrina had to make an effort not to
drop her gaze away.

Then, softly, fleeting, he reached out towards her
and brushed a strand of hair that lay against the
pillow. 'The second message is an unreserved
apology,' he told her, 'for everything that passed
between us this morning. I said things I should
never have said. I behaved like a pig.'

It wasn't the first time he had apologised to her
and she found she rather liked that side of him. He
would go over the top at times, but he was never
above saying sorry.

She shook her head and smiled. 'I'm happy to
accept your apology—but I'm afraid I can't actually
remember what you said!'

It was perfectly true. Their angry exchange over
breakfast had receded to become no more than a
vague blur in her head.

'Once your head clears, you'll remember.' Axel smiled a wry smile. And maybe you won't feel quite so forgiving then.'

'Oh, I'm sure I shall.'

She said it too quickly. She was rather glad when, at that moment, a nurse walked into the room.

'How are you feeling, Miss MacGregor?' As Axel moved out of the way—making Katrina suddenly feel much safer—the pretty dark-haired nurse produced a thermometer and proceeded to give it a vigorous shake.

'I feel OK. Still a little groggy.' Katrina tried to pull herself upright against the pillows.

But the nurse restrained her. 'Just you lie where you are. No physical effort for the moment.' Then she popped the thermometer into Katrina's mouth, took hold of her wrist and proceeded to take her pulse.

Katrina lay, feeling helpless, exchanging an amused glance with Axel, who stood behind the nurse, watching every move she made.

Then the nurse turned to Axel. 'I think you can take her. I'll just have a quick double-check with the doctor.'

'I've already spoken to Dr Lamas. He said there was no problem, just as long as I keep her quiet for the rest of the day.'

'Yes, that's important. You must keep her quiet. No excitement and no strenuous physical exercise.'

Katrina was bursting to ask them what the devil they were talking about! At least they were having the courtesy to talk in English, but for all the sense she could make of what they were saying they might as well have been speaking in Spanish!

Where was Axel supposed to be taking her? What was going on, and why hadn't anybody consulted her? But with the thermometer stuck in her mouth, all she could do was splutter!

Then at last the thermometer was removed. As the nurse glanced at it and nodded her satisfaction, Katrina turned to look at Axel.

'Excuse me,' she said. 'Would you mind explaining? What have you talked to the doctor about? And where am I supposed to be going?'

'You're coming home with me.' Axel smiled at her consternation. 'But don't worry,' he added, as her frown simply deepened. 'It's only for today. Tomorrow I'll set you free.'

'Oh, no, you won't—because I won't be coming!' Katrina's green eyes flashed. 'I'm not going anywhere with you! The only place I'm going is straight back to my hotel.'

'I'm afraid you're not.' Axel narrowed his eyes at her. 'Either you come with me and spend the night at my place, or else you stay right where you are.'

'I'm afraid Mr Jerez is right.' Suddenly the nurse chimed in. 'It wouldn't be a good idea for you to go back to the hotel, where you're alone with nobody to keep an eye on you. You seem to be recovering well, but that was a nasty crack on the head. The doctor has only agreed to discharge you today on condition that you stay with Mr Jerez.'

'But——'

'Pilar will look after you.' Before Katrina could protest, Axel was cutting in to reassure her. 'It's only your welfare I'm concerned about. You really needn't worry about anything else.'

That was a clear enough message, if subtly put. You needn't worry about me making any passes, he was telling her. The arrangement is strictly for the good of your health.

But still Katrina hesitated. She believed what he'd just told her, yet all the same she felt uneasy with the arrangement. For one thing it seemed a bit of an imposition, not to mention just a mite too cosy.

He seemed to read her mind. 'This is not a time for you to be on your own, and I'm the only friend you have on the island.'

Friend? Katrina felt a tingle of pleasure. She rather liked the idea of being classed as his friend.

'Besides,' he was adding, 'you'll be doing Pilar a favour. She enjoys having another woman about the house.'

Katrina wished he hadn't said that. It made her think of his estranged wife and sent a cold sensation sweeping through her. If only, she sighed inwardly, he weren't married.

She banished that thought instantly. He *was* married and intended to stay married. That was the thought she ought to fix in her head.

Then she glanced across at Axel, as he demanded, 'So what's it to be?'

Katrina paused, still undecided. 'I don't know...'

Then the nurse interjected. 'I think you should accept Mr Jerez's offer. Besides, we're short of beds. We could really use one extra.'

'Oh.'

'So, you see, you're really morally obliged.' Axel threw her a teasing wink as she frowned. 'Besides, you'll disappoint Pilar if you don't come. She's already busy making preparations.'

It seemed she really had no choice. Katrina cast him a narrow glance. 'Tomorrow morning I'm moving back to my hotel. This arrangement is definitely just for tonight.'

'Absolutely.' Axel straightened and smiled. 'First thing tomorrow morning you go straight back to your hotel.' He turned to the nurse. 'Perhaps you wouldn't mind getting her things? It looks as though you can have your bed, after all.'

Half an hour later, in a wheelchair, Katrina was leaving the hospital. Personally, she'd thought the wheelchair quite unnecessary—that was, until she'd tried taking a few steps on her own. Instantly, she'd felt decidedly dizzy.

'Don't worry, if you keep quiet, you'll feel fine by tomorrow,' the doctor had told her when he'd come to give her a final check-over. 'Bumps on the head can be dangerous things, though don't worry; I can assure you yours isn't serious.'

Then she'd been loaded into the black Mercedes and, feeling decidedly uneasy just to be sitting alone with him in the car, was being driven by Axel back to the villa.

'I've put you in the main guestroom,' Pilar told her, stepping out of the front door to greet her when they arrived. 'It has a marvellous veranda overlooking the sea and I've put a sofa out on the veranda so you can sit there—unless you'd prefer to go straight to bed?'

'Oh, no, the veranda sounds lovely. I'd much rather sit outside.' Katrina smiled. 'I've already spent long enough in bed today!'

'OK, but just make sure you stay in the shade. Too much sun won't do you any good.' Axel took

her arm, virtually supporting her, as the housekeeper led the way along the corridor to the main
guestroom. 'And if there are any of your things
you need from the hotel, just tell me and I'll go
and pick them up.'

'I'm not sure...'

Katrina, quite frankly, was finding it hard to
think. The way he was supporting her, virtually
carrying her along the corridor, one arm round her
waist, so that she was pressed against him, seemed
to have caused a mild malfunction in her brain.

Not that there was anything at all intimate about
the way he was supporting her—he might have been
a male nurse routinely assisting a patient. The fault
was all hers. She just couldn't help reacting to him.
She longed to reach the veranda, so that he might
release her at last.

Then, finally, to her relief, he was helping her on
to the sofa—which Pilar had already positioned in
the shade. Katrina sank down on to it gratefully.
'This is perfect,' she told Pilar. 'I'm sure I'll re-
cover almost instantly with a wonderful view like
this to look at.'

The view was indeed sublime. From the velvet-
cushioned sofa she could see right out across the
villa gardens to the glittering blue sea beyond. For
the umpteenth time she found herself thinking, This
is paradise.

But Axel was speaking, as he stood there looking
down at her. 'Well, did you decide? Do you want
me to pick up some of your things? Nightdress?
Toilet things? Just say the word. It's no problem.'

'I don't know. I suppose I should at least have
a nightdress and a change of clothes.'

She looked back at him, in spite of herself, re-senting this show of caring. It means nothing, she thought dismally. He would do this for anyone. The only one he really cares for is his wife.

Which is the way it should be, one part of her responded. But she was unable to smother the barren feeling inside her—that bitter barren feeling that marked the end of hope.

He was saying, 'OK, I'll go and pick up a few things. You just lie there and have a good rest. There are some magazines and things if you feel like reading.' He waved to the little table that stood by the sofa. 'And in a minute or two Pilar will bring you something to eat. Just a light snack. I don't think you should eat too much just yet.'

'No, I don't feel very hungry.'

Katrina wished he would go. This show of kindness was beginning to grate on her. If he made one more caring remark her brain would explode.

Then, just in case her tone had been a little sharp, she added, 'Thank you, Pilar. A light snack would be just fine.'

'I'll see you later, then.' At last Axel was leaving. 'Just take it easy,' he reminded her. And then he was gone.

Left alone, Katrina sat back against the cushions and stared unseeingly out to sea. You've got to get to grips with your feelings, she told herself, otherwise you'll end up driving yourself mad.

But there were so many emotions running around in her head—anger, disappointment, gratitude, attraction—that the more she struggled to pin them down the more confused she became.

If only I could just settle on one, she thought despairingly. Anger, preferably. That would make life easier. But it simply wasn't possible to feel undiluted anger towards a man who had just rushed you off to hospital, sat by your bedside until you regained consciousness, then offered you his hospitality until you were fully recovered.

She sighed and closed her eyes. If only the accident hadn't happened.

The warm breeze fanned her face as she lay for a moment and opened her eyes to gaze at the sky. She could remember now quite clearly their quarrel over breakfast—but how could she feel angry about that now? After all, he had apologised.

She sighed again. If only he hadn't apologised.

If only, if only. There were so may if onlys. If only she didn't find him so likeable at times. If only he weren't so charming and so attractive. And, of course, the biggest if only of all. If only he weren't married!

Katrina caught her breath sharply. She must stop thinking like that.

Shaking herself mentally, she reached for one of the magazines that lay on the little table beside the sofa and, determined to distract herself, began flicking through the pages.

But no matter how hard she stared at the pictures and tried to focus her mind on the printed words, she simply could not dispel the grief inside her, nor shake off her despairing sense of loss.

And she could hear the words whispering forlornly about her heart. *If only he weren't married. If only he weren't married.*

* * *

After a light lunch and a brief siesta, Katrina felt a little better and finally managed to put aside her mixed-up feelings and just stretch out lazily in her shady corner and relax.

'You're looking better already,' Pilar told her when in mid-afternoon she brought her some of her favourite pomegranate juice, along with the few bits and pieces Axel had collected from the hotel. 'This morning when you arrived you were looking decidedly peaky.'

'I'm feeling much better.' Katrina stretched and smiled at her. 'In fact, I'm feeling so much better now I'm starting to feel quite lazy about just lying here. I feel I ought to get up and do something useful.'

'You'll do no such thing. You'll stay precisely where you are. Otherwise, you'll be in deep trouble, young lady.'

Katrina swung round at the sound of Axel's voice behind her, feeling her heart slam inside her as she looked into his face. If only, she thought bleakly, gathering herself together, he didn't have this violent physical effect on me. For, as always, at the sight of him her blood was rushing to her head.

He was walking towards her, smiling down at her, his hands in the pockets of his immaculate white trousers. And it was no wonder, Katrina thought, that he affected her the way he did. He really was quite hopelessly handsome, with those broad shoulders and that dark hair and those striking features, all set off to perfection by the open-neck pale blue shirt. But then he affected her the same way whatever he wore!

He came to stand before her. 'Yes, you are looking better.' Then he seated himself in the wicker armchair opposite her. 'Do you mind if I join you for some pomegranate juice?'

'Of course not. Help yourself.' Katrina shifted back against the cushions, making an effort to widen the gap between them. She felt delighted to see him, but was trying hard not to. She said mundanely, 'Have you had a busy day?'

'Busy enough.' Waving Pilar away, Axel helped himself to a glass of fruit juice, drank half of it back and laid the glass down. 'We had a couple of small problems but I think we've sorted them out.'

'Work problems, you mean?'

Her heart had jolted briefly. The minute he'd said the word 'problem' she'd thought of his broken marriage, and of his determination to patch it up.

She tried to push such thoughts away as he answered, 'Yes, work problems. One of our overseas associates was playing us up.'

'I'm sure you don't like that—people playing you up.' Again, to her dismay, she thought of his wife.

'No, I don't like it at all. Fortunately, it doesn't happen a lot.'

'But when it does, I'll bet you soon sort them out.'

'I usually manage to patch things up.'

'I'm sure you can be very persuasive.'

'I have a certain talent.' He paused and smiled suddenly. 'I had no idea you had such faith in me.'

Katrina forced herself to take a deep breath before answering. She felt as though something had taken over in her brain, driving her relentlessly along a path of its choosing. That whole conversation, though Axel didn't know it, had been about his soon-to-be-mended marriage. Stop it! she told herself. You're behaving like a maniac.

She shook herself inwardly and answered calmly, trying not to think of his marriage as she said it, 'I see you as someone who usually gets his own way. If you want something, nine times out of ten you'll get it.'

'Why only nine?' His eyes twinkled, teasing her. 'Is your faith in my powers beginning to slip already?'

'No, but even you must occasionally meet opposition.'

In spite of all her efforts, she saw an image of his wife, slamming out of the car and storming off down the street.

Axel nodded. 'In which case one just has to change tactics. Change tactics and keep calm. One must never get ruffled.'

'I imagine you're rather good at that. Not getting ruffled.'

She remembered how unruffled he'd seemed throughout that scene, sitting there at the driving wheel, his face calmly averted. She'd thought he'd seemed uncaring. But he'd just been changing tactics.

He said, 'I try to be. Getting ruffled doesn't usually help much.'

'You're lucky you can do it.' She was beginning to hate him—and to hate herself for getting so hopelessly ruffled. 'Not everyone can. It takes a certain sort of character.'

'Yes, I suppose it does.'

'A certain sort of will-power.'

The edge to her voice was growing more openly hostile as she felt herself spinning more and more out of control. Suddenly sensing that Axel had become aware of her hostility, and frightened of where her dangerous mood might be leading her, Katrina reached for her fruit juice and took a silencing mouthful.

Then she took a deep breath and said more calmly, 'Well, I'm glad you've sorted out those problems at work.'

'Yes,' he answered. 'I have, more or less.'

Katrina could feel his eyes on her, scrutinising sharply, as she took another mouthful of her fruit juice. And no wonder, she thought. What the devil's got into me? How could I behave like that?

Then, as she sat there with her fingers curled round her glass, the glass drawn almost protectively towards her chest, Axel went on, revealing nothing of what he was thinking,

'As I said, I've sorted out these problems more or less, but there are still one or two details to be hammered out. And I'm afraid that means I'm going to be tied up for dinner.' He smiled regretfully. 'I had hoped to eat at home, but that's out of the question. You're going to have to have dinner on your own.'

'Don't worry, that's no problem.' Katrina felt both relieved and disappointed and was trying her hardest to look totally neutral. 'I don't mind in the least having dinner on my own.'

'Well, as I say, I'm sorry, but I'm afraid it can't be helped.' Axel smiled across at her. 'Pilar's made something special. I'm really rather sorry to be missing out.'

'She shouldn't have bothered.'

'Pilar always bothers. I'm afraid that's just the way she's made.'

Katrina smiled back at him, understanding. 'Yes, I think you're right. She's looked after me wonderfully today.' No one could have looked after her better than Pilar had.

As she said it, for a moment they smiled at one another, their eyes locking together in a shared look of total sympathy. And in that moment an easy warmth flowed between them, curling itself around Katrina's heart. She found herself longing to hang on to that feeling.

Then Axel winked across at her, making her heart twist. 'Yes, you're definitely looking much better,' he said. 'You've got a sparkle in your eyes again and roses in your cheeks. In fact, you're looking a picture of health.'

'I'm definitely feeling better.'

Katrina tried to drag her eyes away, but somehow they refused to detach themselves from his. She continued to gaze at him, her heart full of joy and sorrow, her blood pounding inside her as he asked her, 'Would you like Pilar to bring you your dinner on a tray, or do you feel up to having it in the dining-room?'

'I think I'd like to get up. I feel perfectly able.'

At least she had a moment ago, before the onset of this craziness.

'You could have a table downstairs on the terrace, if you like. That would be more cosy than the dining-room.'

'OK.'

Katrina nodded, still unable to tear her gaze away—though she longed to, for her poor heart was spilling over with emotion. Oh, Axel, she was thinking. Oh, Axel, if only...

But then, to her relief, Axel was rising to his feet. 'And now I'd better leave you. I have to get ready.' He headed for the door. 'Enjoy your dinner.'

Even after he'd gone, the craziness stayed with her, a kind of demented whirring inside her head.

She ate dinner—four courses, which were as delicious as Axel had promised—then sat out on the terrace with a cup of coffee. All evening she'd been struggling in vain to think of other things, but every corner her brain turned there was Axel. And not only Axel, but also Axel's wife. And to think of Axel's wife was a misery and a torment.

I'm driving myself insane, she thought, rising to her feet and walking impatiently to the edge of the terrace. Next thing I know I'll be hearing voices!

'You're still here. Good. I was hoping you would be.'

Her prediction had come true! Katrina spun round with a start, her heart catching in her throat as a deep voice spoke. And she wasn't just hearing voices, it seemed. She was also seeing visions. For standing before her, surely, was a vision? A vision that lifted her heart straight up to heaven.

He was dressed in a dark suit with a white shirt and striped tie, and as always just to look at him took the breath from her body. But it was more than just delight, she felt, far more than just longing. As she looked at him it was as though the shock of his sudden appearance had finally stripped away all the confusion inside her.

I love him, she thought, feeling knocked to her knees with horror.

Out loud she said, 'Axel, what are you doing here?'

'I've brought someone to see you.'

As he motioned to the door behind him, suddenly Katrina was filled with sick panic. It's his wife, she thought, as a shadow moved in the doorway. I know it's his wife and I can't bear to face her.

But there was nothing she could do as a figure stepped out of the shadows.

CHAPTER NINE

BUT it was not Axel's wife. It was someone very different. Katrina recognised him instantly from the photos she had seen of him. It was Axel's brother, Irene's ex-boyfriend, Jaime.

Axel was stepping towards her, laying a hand on her arm. 'I hope you're not too shocked,' he told her kindly. 'I promise I wouldn't have sprung this on you if I hadn't known you were fully recovered.' He smiled. 'Pilar told me about that four-course dinner.'

Katrina was very glad she'd had it. On an empty stomach she might have found this all a little hard to cope with!

She continued to stare at Jaime who was standing awkwardly in the doorway. 'What's going on?' she stammered. 'What's he doing here?'

'He's come to see you. He has something to give you.'

The sudden hard edge to Axel's voice caused Katrina to turn and glance at him. His eyes were fixed on Jaime, his expression dark and angry. She had never seen such a look of contempt in a man's face.

He made an impatient gesture with his head at Jaime. 'What are you waiting for?' he growled. 'Katrina wants to know what you've come for.'

Jaime shuffled forward, looking like humiliation personified. And as Katrina looked into his face

she found it hard to believe that this man was really
Axel's brother. His features were not dissimilar and
he had the same dark colouring, but everything else
about him was somehow less.

It wasn't simply that he was a centimetre or two
shorter and lacked his brother's powerful aura. The
lack was in the features of his handsome but weak
face. He was a lesser man than his brother in every
respect.

He stepped cautiously towards Katrina, avoiding
looking at Axel. 'I've come to give you this.' He
stuck one hand into his pocket and produced a
folded piece of paper. 'It's a cheque for the six
thousand pounds Irene gave me.'

He held it out to her and started to add, 'I never
intended to keep it. I——'

But that was as far as he got. Axel cut in, taking
an impatient step towards him. 'Spare us more lies.'
His tone was unforgiving. 'And now that you've
done what you came for, kindly get out of my
house.'

'Don't worry, I'm going.' Jaime cast him a
resentful look, then instantly, uncomfortably,
snatched his eyes away. The next minute, in an un-
convincing parody of arrogance, he was turning and
disappearing back inside the villa.

'I suppose I have you to thank for this?' Katrina
sank down on the arm of a nearby chair and glanced
at the cheque. 'I'm really most grateful. I'd re-
signed myself to never seeing this money again.'

But Axel was shaking his head. 'I really don't
think you ought to thank me. On the contrary, you
ought to be mad at me. It's my fault you didn't get
your money back sooner.'

Katrina glanced up at him. 'Why?' she queried. Though she suspected she knew the answer.

With a wry smile Axel confirmed what she was thinking. 'I knew all along where my brother was hiding. I deliberately conspired to keep you from him.'

He paused and with a sigh slipped his hands into his trouser pockets. 'Look, I have a bit of explaining to do and I suggest I do it over a brandy.' He looked at her. 'Unless, of course, you'd rather just go straight to bed?'

'Definitely not.' Katrina smiled and shook her head at him. 'I can't wait to hear what you have to tell me. Besides,' she added, 'I'm not the least bit tired. In fact, I've never felt more awake.'

'You're sure?' He leaned closer. 'How's the head?'

'The head's perfectly OK.' But suddenly her poor heart wasn't. It was racing inside her like an out-of-control express train. All he was doing was taking a look at her bruise, but he was leaning so close she caught the cool masculine scent of him and could almost count the silky dark lashes that framed his eyes.

Her heart turned over helplessly. I really do love him, she thought.

She cleared her throat huskily and tried to sound normal. 'As you can see, I've removed the bandage. I don't think it looks too bad.'

'It's still pretty swollen.'

He tilted her chin to see better, his fingers sending fireballs of sensation across her skin and a hopeless bleak despair through her heart.

'Are you sure it isn't painful?' he was saying.

'Only if I shake my head too hard.'

He smiled. 'I'll remember that. And I'll make a point of not saying anything likely prompt such a reaction.'

Then he released her. 'OK, let's have that brandy. You make yourself comfortable. I won't be a minute.'

As he headed for the drawing-room, Katrina watched him go, her heart tugging painfully inside her. I'm a fool, she thought. How could I have let it happen? How could I have allowed myself to fall in love with a man I know I can never ever have?

She stood up from the chair arm and seated herself against the cushions and stared with a sigh out to the horizon. She must try to be philosophical, for there was nothing to hope for. Axel was unconditionally out of bounds.

But at least for the few more days I'm here, she consoled herself, I shall allow myself to love him from a distance. It wasn't much, but it was better than nothing.

'Here you are.'

He had reappeared silently and was standing at her side, making her heart shift as she turned to look at him, and holding out a balloon of brandy.

She took it, feeling another quick dart inside her as his fingers, ever so fleetingly, brushed against hers. Then he was turning to seat himself in the armchair opposite. He raised his glass to her. 'Cheers!' he said.

Katrina raised her own glass. 'Cheers!' she smiled back at him.

'Do you mind if I remove my jacket?' Axel took a mouthful of his brandy and laid the glass down on a nearby table. Then as Katrina shook her head, he shrugged off the dark jacket and loosened the striped silk tie at his throat. 'That's the trouble with these formal business dinners,' he told her. 'You always have to wear a suit.'

'Well, at least it didn't last long—your business dinner, I mean.' Katrina glanced at her watch as she took a sip from her own glass, then laid it down on the table beside his. 'It's only just after half-past ten. I didn't expect you back as early as this.'

'And I wouldn't be back, except the meeting fell apart.' Axel made a face as he reached for his brandy glass again, took a mouthful and leaned back in his armchair, his dark hair as glossy as silk beneath the moonlight. 'My dinner guest walked out in a huff, I'm afraid, before we were halfway through our steaks. He didn't much care for the terms I was demanding.' He smiled a wry smile. 'It was quite a dramatic little scene.'

'It certainly sounds like it.' Katrina smiled sympathetically. 'So what did you do? Did you just leave as well?'

'I finished my steak first—and most of the wine.' He smiled again, his dark eyes dancing. 'It happened to be a particularly good vintage. It went against the grain to waste it.'

Katrina laughed at that. 'Quite right!' she agreed. 'One should never waste a bottle of good wine.'

As Axel laughed with her, a flare of sympathy passed between them. 'One should never waste anything that's good,' he told her.

He held her gaze a moment, sending a bitter-sweet sensation curling, warm and shivery, around Katrina's heart.

We have something good, she was thinking. A warmth has grown between us. We can never be more, but perhaps we can be friends. Over the days that remained, perhaps she'd have that to enjoy, at least.

He was continuing to watch her. 'And now,' he said. 'I think it's time I offered you those explanations I promised.'

His expression, as he spoke, had suddenly grown more serious. Katrina watched him as he glanced down into his brandy glass and wondered what might be coming next.

'The first thing I want to say is that I deeply regret the way I've treated you over the past few days—giving you the run-around where Jaime was concerned.'

As he said it, he looked up at her with an expression of such remorse that, just for a moment, Katrina felt quite startled.

He shook his head. 'You see, I didn't believe your sister's story about the missing six thousand pounds. I couldn't believe my own brother could have done such a thing.'

Katrina nodded. 'I can understand that,' she said.

Axel smiled a grateful smile, then grew serious again. 'Don't think I didn't confront him with your story. I did, after the very first day you came here. But he swore it was all nonsense, that there'd never been any money, never any talk of starting any business, that your sister had made the whole thing up.'

He stared into his brandy glass again and was silent for a moment. 'And, fool that I was, I believed him,' he added.

'You shouldn't blame yourself.' Katrina hated to
see that pained look that suddenly was shadowing
the strong vital features. 'It's only natural to trust
one's own brother or sister. No one expects lies from
a member of one's own family.'

'No, one doesn't.' Axel continued to stare into
his brandy glass. 'Although, knowing my brother,
I should have been less trusting. He has a habit of
letting people down.'

He sighed. 'Which is why I decided to confront
him again, this time—shall we say?—a little more
forcefully. That was this afternoon, in between
business meetings. In the end, he cracked and
admitted the truth.'

Katrina found herself smiling. 'I almost feel sorry
for him. I suspect poor old Jaime is no match for
you.'

Axel paused and met her eyes and a look passed
between them, another of those looks of shared
sympathy and humour. Katrina had to swallow hard
on the sudden lump in her throat.

Then Axel was saying, 'I know it probably
doesn't mean much, but I'm genuinely sorry about
what he did to your sister. I realise now that he
treated her very badly.'

Well, this was a pretty turn-around! Katrina
couldn't resist pointing out to him, 'I thought you
believed she deserved all she got?'

'I did, but I realise now I was wrong about that
too.' Something flickered at the back of his eyes as
he said it. For a split-second it seemed to Katrina
he was about to add something. But, instead, he
dropped his gaze again and simply told her, 'I think,
as it turns out, I misjudged your sister.'

'Yes, I think you did.' That momentary flicker had made her curious. And as she frowned at him suddenly Katrina remembered something.

'Yet you were so sure she was no good,' she put to him accusingly. 'I remember you suggesting to me that you knew something about her that would make it very easy for you to *prove* to me that she was a liar, yet you never actually told me what that something was.'

She paused and fixed him with a searching look. 'Was there really something or was that just a slander?'

He did not answer immediately and he did not look at her. Then he shrugged. 'I'm afraid it was just a slander.' Then he raised his eyes and smiled at her appealingly. 'Forgive me,' he said. 'I really am sorry.'

'Don't worry, I forgive you.'

How could she have done otherwise? How could one not forgive the person one loved?

She felt a rush of fierce love for him gather round her heart. She had never loved him more than she loved him at that moment.

Axel reached for his brandy glass and swallowed back the contents. 'I'm glad that's out of the way,' he said.

Katrina nodded, glad too. It was one less barrier between them. She just wished with all her heart there were no barriers at all.

He was watching her, half smiling, making her smile back at him. Katrina sensed there was something going on in his head.

Then he laid down his glass and leaned towards
her slightly. 'What are you doing tomorrow?' he
asked.

'I'll be interviewing Loughlin.'

Her heart gave a small flicker.

'But you won't be tied up all day with Loughlin,
surely?' There was a frown between his brows as
he waited for her answer.

'I don't think so.'

The flickering had turned into a flutter. Was he
about to invite her to dinner?

He smiled. 'I think you should take it easy
tomorrow.' He held her eyes a moment, making the
fluttering grow stronger. Then he detached his gaze
and moved back in his chair slightly.

'Unfortunately, I won't be here to oversee you.
I'm afraid this evening's little débâcle means I'm
going to have to fly to Basle tomorrow morning to
try and sort the whole mess out.'

The fluttering had stopped abruptly and Katrina's
smile had died. Her features felt frozen as though
touched by icy fingers.

She said in a dull voice, 'You're going to
Switzerland tomorrow? How long do you expect to
be away?'

'Two or three days. As long as it takes. That's
why,' he added, glancing at her again, 'I decided
to drag Jaime to see you this evening. I'd planned
to do it tomorrow, once you were feeling better.
But the way things stand now I probably won't see
you again—you'll likely have gone by the time I get
back. So I had no choice. It had to be tonight.'

Katrina sensed she had gone as pale as the stucco
walls behind her and was glad that in the semi-

darkness Axel couldn't see. She was even gladder he couldn't see inside her heart, for suddenly it was wrenching and weeping in helpless pain.

It took all of her strength just to murmur, 'I see.'

'I phoned Pilar first, just to check that you were up to the shock.' He was continuing as though this was an ordinary conversation, unaware that every word of it was tearing her apart. 'She told me you were much better, more or less back to normal, and that you'd just consumed a four-course dinner.'

He smiled a teasing smile as he added that last part and Katrina forced herself to dredge up a wan smile in response.

She said tritely, 'No wonder. It was a delicious dinner.'

This is the last time I shall ever see him, she was thinking in dull misery. These few moments here and now are the only moments I have left. To know that was like laying a bare foot on broken glass.

'You see,' he was continuing, 'I knew it wouldn't be enough just for me to give you the cheque. I knew I had to get Jaime to do it personally. Otherwise, even with his signature on the cheque, you would have suspected the money came from me.'

He paused and threw her a knowing look. 'I think you'll agree I'm right about that?'

Katrina felt numb from head to toe. Her brain was reeling. She wanted to reach out and take a slug of her brandy. But she was afraid she might spill it, for she was sure her hands were shaking.

She looked across at him, suddenly wishing with all her heart that she could just close her eyes and disappear.

'So, that's why I had to bring him here tonight.' Axel frowned suddenly and leaned with a concerned look towards her. 'Katrina, are you sure you're OK?'

'Perfectly OK. I was just listening to what you were saying.'

So, after all, he had noticed the sudden change in her, and now he was rising to his feet and apologising. 'You're tired. I should have known better. I've kept you up too late.' To her dismay, he was reaching out to offer her his hand. 'Come,' he was saying. 'It's time you were in bed.'

Katrina ignored his proffered hand—she would weep if he touched her—and, pulling herself together, rose shakily to her feet.

'You're right,' she agreed, not daring to look at him. 'Suddenly I am a little tired.'

He was leading her across the drawing-room. 'What you need is a good night's rest. I had no business keeping you up so late.' Then, out in the hallway, he turned towards her. 'Look, I just want to assure to you one more time that I really am sorry for everything that's happened.'

To her total dismay he reached out and touched her arm.

'That's OK. I understand.'

The way he was looking down at her was causing her heart to break into pieces. And as his fingers continued to burn into her flesh, Katrina had to breathe very carefully and blink the tears away.

Then he was saying, 'I hope your meeting with Fergus goes well. Have a good night's sleep and I hope you feel better in the morning.'

'Oh, I'm sure I'll feel fine.'

She glanced up into his face, knowing she would never feel fine again.

But already he was drawing away, dropping his hand from her arm. 'I'll leave you now. I have to make a phone call.' He paused briefly. 'I'll say goodnight—and goodbye.'

He did not wait. Already he was leaving, heading on swift strides back into the drawing-room.

Katrina watched him go. 'Goodnight,' she whispered. She could not bring herself to say goodbye.

Then, scarcely breathing, she climbed the stairs to her bedroom, her heart suddenly as heavy as lead within her, her soul wrapped in a shroud of grey despair.

Two days later Katrina's work was done and the time had come for her to leave Tenerife.

Her interviews with Fergus Loughlin and his friends had gone swimmingly, better than she could ever possibly have imagined. Everything was set up and suitable locations picked out so that the filming of the programme could go ahead. Her colleagues in Edinburgh were delighted when she phoned them.

And though Katrina was pleased with what she had achieved, somehow it felt like a hollow victory. Her part was over now. She would not be one of the team who came to do the actual job. She would never set foot on Tenerife again. And never again would she set eyes on Axel.

But that was a good thing, she kept trying to tell herself. By leaving the island perhaps she would rid herself of the terrible pain that tormented her constantly.

For it had never left her. Not for a moment. And there were times when it was so fierce that she thought it would kill her. Could one really endure such agony and not die?

But, at least, she had not much longer to endure. In a matter of a few short hours she'd be gone.

There was one more thing, however, that Katrina wanted to do before she booked a taxi to the airport. She wanted to thank Pilar for all her kindness. With just a small gesture. A bunch of flowers.

She'd thought about it and thought about it. Should she have them delivered or should she take them round to the villa herself? The former solution seemed a little impersonal, especially since the villa was just a short taxi-ride away and she had plenty of time to do the job herself. But she suspected her own motives in her desire to deliver them personally. Was she really just hoping to see Axel one more time?

He probably isn't back yet, she told her reflection, as she peered at herself critically in the mirror. And, even if he is, what difference would it make? The chances of his actually being at the villa were small. And if he was at home, even then it would make no difference. And if it did any harm, it would only be to herself.

Katrina sighed and frowned. Could she bear to see him again? Could she bear the pain of a second parting? Was it really wise to take such a risk?

Then she dropped her gaze away. It wasn't wise at all, but still it was a risk she knew she had to take. Any risk would be worth one final precious glimpse of him. It was shameful, but the truth was she would risk anything for that.

Her heart was clamouring as, clutching her
bouquet of flowers for Pilar, Katrina climbed into
the taxi and headed for the villa. And by the time
they turned the corner into the huge grounds, the
clamouring had grown so furious that she was surprised the taxi driver couldn't hear it.

It was then that, belatedly, sanity hit her. She
closed her eyes. Please don't let Axel be here! To
see him again—or worse, to have to speak to him—
was more than she could cope with. It would kill
her.

If she'd had the strength to speak, she'd have
asked the driver to turn round. What she was doing
was utter folly. She should never have risked it. But,
already, it was too late. They were drawing up
outside the front door. With trembling fingers she
reached for the door-handle.

'Wait for me here, please.' Miraculously, she
found her voice again, as she climbed out of the
cab and addressed the driver. 'I'll only be a couple
of minutes.'

Then on legs so weak they could barely hold her
she was hurrying up the wide stone steps to the front
door.

Pilar opened up instantly and beamed with delight to see her. '*Señorita*, how nice to see you
again!'

'It's nice to see you, too.' Katrina smiled back at
her, suddenly glad she'd made this rash gesture,
after all. She thrust the bouquet of flowers into the
housekeeper's arms. 'I'm leaving in a couple of
hours and I wanted to give you these. Just a little
gift to say thank you for looking after me.'

'But, *señorita*, that was nothing.' Tears sprang to the woman's eyes. 'It was my pleasure to look after you, just as it is my pleasure to see you now.' She paused and blinked the tears away. 'Señor Jerez will be sorry he's missed you.'

'You mean he's not back yet?' It was what Katrina had thought she wanted, but there was no denying the stab of disappointment. Suddenly the sky seemed to darken a little.

'He'll be home tomorrow night. What a pity you're going to miss him.' Then with a broad smile Pilar looked down at her flowers again. 'These are too beautiful. Really, you're so kind!'

It was at that moment that there was a movement in the hall behind Pilar, and suddenly, arm in arm, laughing and smiling at each other, a dark-haired young woman and a man appeared.

Katrina felt her jaw drop as she recognised the woman instantly. It was Axel's wife, the woman she had seen with him in the car. But the man whose lips she was reaching up to kiss quickly was a fair-haired young man whom Katrina had never seen before.

She felt a rush of outrage on Axel's behalf. How dared his wife behave this way, flaunting her lover like this in his absence? Did she have no shame at all?

Then a sad thought occurred to her. She frowned. Poor Axel. It looked as though his efforts to save his marriage had failed.

The couple said something to Pilar, evidently bidding her farewell, then with a carefree smile at the scowling Katrina they were heading off down the driveway together to where a little sports car was parked. Katrina watched them go. Poor Axel, she thought again.

She turned back to Pilar and was surprised to see her smiling. Didn't the housekeeper know how much her boss wanted his wife back? Then Pilar proceeded to surprise her even more.

'Señor Jerez will be so pleased when he hears the news about his sister.' She glanced again at the departing couple and beamed from ear to ear. 'There's not going to be any divorce, after all. She and her husband are back together.'

For a bewildered moment Katrina simply stared at her, not believing what she was hearing. Then she just managed to squeak, 'That woman is Axel's sister? Do you mean to tell me she isn't his wife?'

'She's his sister, Ana.' Pilar laughed with amusement. 'Señor Jerez has no wife!' Then, unaware of Katrina's stunned expression, she glanced down, smiling, at her flowers again. 'Thank you again for these—and have a safe flight home.'

Katrina climbed into her taxi and waved goodbye, feeling like a sleepwalker, barely aware of what she was doing. Nothing quite made sense, yet a couple of simple facts shone out like beacons amidst the darkness.

The woman she had thought was Axel's wife was his sister. And the divorce they had discussed was his sister's, not his. She scarcely dared believe it, though Pilar had said it quite clearly. Axel wasn't married, after all!

She sat back in her seat and felt like weeping. This was the miracle she'd so desperately hoped for—but what good was it to her now when she would never see him again?

CHAPTER TEN

BACK at her hotel, in a hopeless daze, Katrina busied herself packing up her things. What a fool I am, she kept thinking over and over. I jumped to all the wrong conclusions. Axel's as free as I am. He doesn't have a wife.

Grief and longing filled her, so fierce that she could scarcely bear it. As a result of her folly what she'd done was push away the only man she'd ever wanted in her life. That thought was like a fist crushing her into the floor.

Her packing done, Katrina paced restlessly up and down. There was still an hour before the taxi came to take her to the airport and she knew she would go mad if she stayed cooped up in her room. On an impulse she grabbed her room key and headed for the door. I'll go down to the terrace coffee shop and have something to drink, she thought.

When the lift stopped at the ground floor she stepped out into the lobby, pausing to glance neither to left nor to right. Then she was heading for the glass doors that led out on to the terrace, her hand reaching out to pull the door open.

But another hand grasped the door-handle an instant before hers. She half turned to say thank you and stopped dead in her tracks.

'Let's find a quiet corner. I want to talk.'

179

Katrina froze to the spot, her heart crashing inside her. 'What are you doing here?' she demanded croakily. 'I thought you were still in Basle.'

'Well, I'm not. I came back early. And if you ask me, it's just as well.'

As he spoke, Axel had taken hold of her firmly by the elbow and was steering through the door and towards a table in a corner. And it was really just as well, Katrina was thinking. She was still so stunned she wasn't sure if she'd have managed the journey on her own.

Once they were seated, he wasted no time with polite preliminaries.

He leaned towards her, frowning. 'Is it true,' he put to her, 'that you were under the impression I was married? And what on earth gave you such a ridiculous idea?'

Katrina could scarcely believe that any of this was happening. Less than five minutes ago she'd believed she'd never see him again, and now here he was, sitting right in front of her. She kept wanting to touch him to make sure he was real.

She said. 'How did you find out? Did Pilar tell you?'

'Yes, Pilar told me, almost by accident. She was telling me that my sister and her husband had called to tell me about their reconciliation, and she just happened to add laughingly that you'd thought Ana was my wife.'

He shook his head at her almost fiercely. 'Kindly explain how on earth you got hold of that idea?'

'I saw you together once. I saw you fighting...'

'You told me that, but you also told me you knew who she was.'

'I know. I thought I did. To me it looked like a marital quarrel.' She bit her lip. What an idiot she'd been!

Axel was shaking his head again. 'Some marital quarrel! What I'd been doing was trying to give Ana some brotherly advice and persuade her to go back to her husband. She ended up screaming at me and slamming out of the car.' He sighed. 'And you concluded from that that we were married?'

'Well, not immediately. I thought that maybe she was a girlfriend. It was at the dinner party that I got the impression you were married...' Katrina threw her mind back. 'I made some comment to Sofía about where was the hostess...' She blushed as she said it. At the time she'd been fishing. 'And Sofía said something about we won't be seeing her again and added how sad it was about the marriage break-up.'

Katrina looked down into her lap. 'That was when I put two and two together. I assumed the hostess was your wife and that your marriage had broken up.'

'Well, you assumed all wrong.' Axel reached out suddenly and tilted her chin so that she was looking at him. 'The hostess was my sister. It's become a bit of a tradition that when I have dinner parties my sister takes charge of things. She enjoys it and I'm only too happy to let her get on with it.' He sighed. 'But we fell out when she separated from her husband. I knew she was making a big mistake and she was furious with me for saying so. She swore she'd never set foot in my house again.'

'Well, she seems to have changed her mind.' Katrina's skin was tingling where Axel's fingers were holding her chin. It was a feeling she longed to feel all over.

'Yes. I'm glad to say everything's back to normal.' He smiled briefly, then frowned again. 'But it's you we're here to talk about. How could you believe that I was married?'

'I told you.' Katrina flushed. His hold on her chin had tightened. She almost added, 'I didn't want to believe it.' But she bit the words back. They would be too revealing.

Instead, she said, as lightly as she could manage, 'I keep seeing you with all these different women. You can't blame me if I find it a little hard to keep track.'

'You've seen me with two. My sister and my sister-in-law—and instantly jumped to the wrong conclusion about both!' He smiled. 'First, you assume my sister-in-law's my girlfriend, then you go and marry me off to my own sister!'

He shook his head at her, then suddenly his expression became sober. 'But there's still something I ought to tell you about my sister-in-law, Maria. I haven't been strictly honest about that.'

What on earth did he mean? Katrina looked at him anxiously. What could he possibly be about to tell her now?

There was a pained look in his eyes. He ran his fingers through his hair. 'Look, I know you're not going to like this, but I think it's time I told you the truth.'

Then, before Katrina could say a thing, he took a deep breath. 'The truth is that Maria is Jaime's wife.'

'Jaime's wife?' Katrina gaped at him, shocked.
'Jaime's wife?' she gasped again. 'But I assumed
she was married to one of your other brothers! Are
you telling me now that Jaime's married?' She fell
back in her seat, totally winded. 'I can't believe it!
Are you telling me the truth?'

'Yes, I'm afraid I am.' Axel's gaze was
sympathetic. 'I knew you wouldn't like it, but yes,
Maria is his wife.'

He sighed and sat back a little in his seat. 'It was
in order to protect Maria that I kept you from
Jaime. She loves him and knows nothing about all
his infidelities, and that's the way I intend to keep
it. When you arrived on the scene, demanding to
see him, I was terrified you might turn up on his
doorstep some time when Maria was around and
create a scene. She has enough to suffer without
that.'

Katrina was shaking her head, struggling to take
this in. 'But I thought you were keeping me from
him because you didn't believe me about the
money?'

'No, I didn't believe you at first and I've told
you the reason why.' Axel smiled a wry smile. 'I
realise now I was crazy. After all the lies my
brother's told me over the years, after all the stories
he's invented to wangle money out of me—stories
I fell for until I started to get wise to him—I should
have known better than to take his word.'

He shrugged sadly. 'But he's my brother, and
there's a part of me that keeps hoping that maybe,
finally, he's changed.'

He was silent for a moment, then he regarded
her frankly. 'But you're wrong to think I protected

him because I didn't believe you. If it hadn't been for Maria, I would have just let him get on with it. He's old enough to handle his own life, after all. But I couldn't just stand by and see Maria destroyed.'

Through her sense of shock Katrina suddenly felt quite moved. 'She's very lucky to have a brother-in-law like you.'

Axel actually looked embarrassed by the compliment, a reaction which simply touched Katrina even more. With all her heart she longed to reach out and kiss him.

But he was continuing, 'There's something else I ought to tell you. It may help you understand some of the things I said.' As he watched her, there was a look of self-reproach in his eyes. 'I believed,' he told her, 'that your sister knew Jaime was married. He swore to me a hundred times that he'd told her.' He made a face. 'That explains my low opinion of her. An opinion, I can now tell you, I have completely revised. All I can do is apologise on my brother's behalf for the disgraceful way he's treated Irene.'

'You don't need to apologise. It's not your fault.' Katrina watched the dark remorseful face with sympathy. 'Did Jaime finally tell you the truth about that as well the other day when he admitted that he'd taken the money?'

Axel nodded. 'Yes, I finally squeezed the whole truth out of him.' He looked across at her. 'I realised almost from the beginning that you had no idea that Jaime was married. That was the lie I threatened to expose—that your sister had deceived you by not telling you that.'

'So, what stopped you from telling me?'

Axel shrugged. 'You seemed so attached to Irene. I thought if I told you it might change your feelings for her, and I didn't want to be responsible for that.'

Katrina felt another sharp twist at her heart. Such thoughtfulness. Such kindness. And she had never suspected for a minute.

'Thank you,' she told him. Then she shook her head. 'But I would never have accepted that Irene knew he was married. I know she's not that kind of girl.' Then she sighed and added, 'I suppose we can only be glad she's finally out of that little mess.'

'Yes, there's that much to be grateful for.' Then suddenly he leaned forward and gazed long and deeply into her eyes. 'It would appear that you're not that kind of girl, either.' A flicker crossed his eyes. 'Is that the reason why you kept pushing me away every time I came near you? Because you believed that I was married?'

Katrina nodded, flushing. 'Yes,' she said.

A look of relief touched his eyes, then a little tentatively he smiled. 'What about all that disgust you kept telling me about? Wasn't that part of the reason, too?'

Karina's flush grew deeper. She shook her head. 'I'm afraid I invented the disgust,' she confessed.

He reached out and took her hand. 'I'm happy to hear it. I confess you had me worried a couple of times.' Then his expression relaxed. 'You and I, *querida*, have a very great deal to discuss, I would say. And I suggest we discuss it all on our journey to Edinburgh.'

'*Our* journey to Edinburgh? You mean you're going with me?' Katrina laughed delightedly. She could scarcely believe what she was hearing.

'Of course I'm coming with you.' Axel drew her to her feet. 'I don't intend letting you out of my sight for a minute. And, besides, it's a while since I had a few days in Scotland.' He glanced at his watch. 'I think it's time we were moving. But, before we do, there's just one more thing...'

And, right there on the terrace before a delighted audience, he swept her into his arms and kissed her. Then he held her close to him for a moment.

'I love you,' he told her, making her heart burst inside her. 'More than you can ever know.'

They were flying over Paris when Axel proposed to her.

'Marry me,' he murmured, taking hold of her hand. 'I know this is rather sudden... Maybe you think I'm rushing you... But I've never been so sure of anything in my life.'

Katrina felt her breath catch. She looked into his eyes and smiled at him, her heart filled to the brim with love and happiness.

'It is sudden,' she nodded. 'And, yes, you are rushing me.' She let her eyes drift over him, adoring every inch of him. 'But I've never been so sure of anything in my life either...'

She leaned across and kissed him tenderly on the lips. 'So the answer is yes. I'll be your wife.'

'You mean that? Truly?'

'With all my heart I mean it.'

She sighed as he reached for her and drew her against him, kissing her and circling her gently with his arms. 'I'm so lucky,' she told him, gazing into his eyes.

'Yes, you are.' For a moment the dark eyes teased her. Then he held his breath and tightened his arms round her. 'But there's not a soul in the whole world half as lucky as I am.'

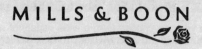

MILLS & BOON

Proudly present...

This is a remarkable achievement for a writer who had her
first Mills & Boon novel published in 1973. Some six million
words later and with sales around the world, her novels
continue to be popular with romance fans everywhere.

Her centenary romance '*VAMPIRE LOVER*' is a suspense-
filled story of dark desires and tangled emotions—Charlotte
Lamb at her very best.

Published: June 1994   **Price: £1.90**

Next Month's Romances

Each month you can choose from a wide variety of romance with Mills & Boon. Below are the new titles to look out for next month, why not ask either Mills & Boon Reader Service or your Newsagent to reserve you a copy of the titles you want to buy – just tick the titles you would like and either post to Reader Service or take it to any Newsagent and ask them to order your books.

Please save me the following titles:	Please tick	✓
PASSIONATE OPPONENT	Jenny Cartwright	
AN IMPOSSIBLE DREAM	Emma Darcy	
SHATTERED WEDDING	Elizabeth Duke	
A STRANGER'S KISS	Liz Fielding	
THE FURY OF LOVE	Natalie Fox	
THE LAST ILLUSION	Diana Hamilton	
DANGEROUS DESIRE	Sarah Holland	
STEPHANIE	Debbie Macomber	
BITTER MEMORIES	Margaret Mayo	
A TASTE OF PASSION	Kristy McCallum	
PHANTOM LOVER	Susan Napier	
WEDDING BELLS FOR BEATRICE	Betty Neels	
DARK VICTORY	Elizabeth Oldfield	
LOVE'S STING	Catherine Spencer	
CHASE A DREAM	Jennifer Taylor	
EDGE OF DANGER	Patricia Wilson	

If you would like to order these books in addition to your regular subscription from Mills & Boon Reader Service please send £1.90 per title to: Mills & Boon Reader Service, Freepost, P.O. Box 236, Croydon, Surrey, CR9 9EL, quote your Subscriber No:................................... (if applicable) and complete the name and address details below. Alternatively, these books are available from many local Newsagents including W H Smith, J Menzies, Martins and other paperback stockists from 8 July 1994.

Name:...

Address:..

....Post Code:........................

To Retailer: If you would like to stock M&B books please contact your regular book/magazine wholesaler for details.

You may be mailed with offers from other reputable companies as a result of this application. If you would rather not take advantage of these opportunities please tick box. ☐

SUMMER SPECIAL!

Four exciting new Romances for the price of three

Each Romance features British heroines and their encounters with dark and desirable Mediterranean men. *Plus, a free Elmlea recipe booklet inside every pack.*

So sit back and enjoy your sumptuous summer reading pack and indulge yourself with the free Elmlea recipe ideas.

Available July 1994   Price £5.70

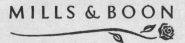

MILLS & BOON

Accept 4 FREE Romances and 2 FREE gifts

FROM READER SERVICE

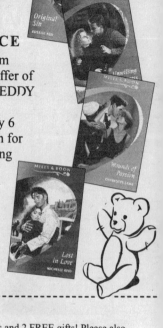

Here's an irresistible invitation from Mills & Boon. Please accept our offer of 4 FREE Romances, a CUDDLY TEDDY and a special MYSTERY GIFT! Then, if you choose, go on to enjoy 6 captivating Romances every month for just £1.90 each, postage and packing FREE. Plus our FREE Newsletter with author news, competitions and much more.

Send the coupon below to: Mills & Boon Reader Service, FREEPOST, PO Box 236, Croydon, Surrey CR9 9EL.

- -

NO STAMP REQUIRED

Yes! Please rush me 4 FREE Romances and 2 FREE gifts! Please also reserve me a Reader Service subscription. If I decide to subscribe I can look forward to receiving 6 brand new Romances for just £11.40 each month, post and packing FREE. If I decide not to subscribe I shall write to you within 10 days - I can keep the free books and gifts whatever I choose. I may cancel or suspend my subscription at any time. I am over 18 years of age.

Ms/Mrs/Miss/Mr _____ EP70R

Address _____

_____

Postcode _____ Signature _____